Taste of Home
Diabetic
Cookbook 2008

Taste of Home Books

Copyright © 2008 Publications International, Ltd.
Cover photo, back cover text and text on pages 4–7 copyright © 2008 Reiman Media Group, Inc.
All rights reserved. This publication may not be reproduced or quoted in whole or in part by any means whatsoever without written permission from:

Louis Weber, CEO
Publications International, Ltd.
7373 North Cicero Avenue
Lincolnwood, IL 60712

Permission is never granted for commercial purposes.

Taste of Home is a registered trademark of Reiman Media Group, Inc.

SUNKIST is a registered trademark of Sunkist Growers, Inc.

All recipes and photographs that contain specific brand names are copyrighted by those companies and/or associations, unless otherwise specified. All photographs *except* that on page 97 copyright © Publications International, Ltd.

Some of the products listed in this publication may be in limited distribution.

Recipe selection by Reiman Publications.

Vice President, Executive Editor/Books: Heidi Reuter Lloyd
Senior Editor/Books: Mark Hagen
Food Director: Diane Werner, R.D.
Recipe Editor: Christine Rukavena
Food Editor: Peggy Woodward, R.D.
Creative Director: Ardyth Cope
Senior Vice President, Editor in Chief: Catherine Cassidy
President, Food & Entertaining: Suzanne M. Grimes
President and Chief Executive Officer: Mary G. Berner

Front cover photography by Reiman Media Group, Inc.
Photographer: Jim Wieland

Photography on pages 30, 33, 48, 59 and 63 by PDR Productions.

Recipe Development on pages 49, 50, 59, 60 and 63 by Jackie Mills, M.S., R.D.; on pages 32 and 35 by Marcia Kay Stanley, M.S., R.D.

Pictured on the front cover: Strawberry-Peach Cream Puffs *(page 167).*

Pictured on the back cover *(clockwise from top right):* Ham and Vegetable Omelet *(page 60),* Vegetable Fajitas with Spicy Salsa *(page 83)* and Turkey Shanghai *(page 98).*

ISBN-13: 978-1-4127-2686-3
ISBN-10: 1-4127-2686-7

ISSN: 1554-0103

Manufactured in China.

8 7 6 5 4 3 2 1

Nutritional Analysis: Every effort has been made to check the accuracy of the nutritional information that appears with each recipe. However, because numerous variables account for a wide range of values for certain foods, nutritive analyses in this book should be considered approximate. Different results may be obtained by using different nutrient databases and different brand-name products.

Microwave Cooking: Microwave ovens vary in wattage. Use the cooking times as guidelines and check for doneness before adding more time.

Preparation/Cooking Times: Preparation times are based on the approximate amount of time required to assemble the recipe before cooking, baking, chilling or serving. These times include preparation steps such as measuring, chopping and mixing. The fact that some preparations and cooking can be done simultaneously is taken into account. Preparation of optional ingredients and serving suggestions is not included.

Note: This book is for informational purposes and is not intended to provide medical advice. Neither Publications International, Ltd., nor the authors, editors or publisher takes responsibility for any possible consequences from any treatment, procedure, exercise, dietary modification, action, or applications of medication or preparation by any person reading or following the information in this cookbook. The publication of this book does not constitute the practice of medicine, and this cookbook does not replace your physician, pharmacist or health-care specialist. **Before undertaking any course of treatment or nutritional plan, the authors, editors and publisher advise the reader to check with a physician or other health-care provider.**

Not all recipes in this cookbook are appropriate for all people with diabetes. Health-care providers, registered dietitians and certified diabetes educators can help design specific meal plans tailored to individual needs.

Taste of Home
Diabetic
Cookbook 2008

Personalizing Your Healthy Lifestyle

Chicken Veggie Pasta (page 65)

EAT WELL...FEEL GREAT!

Bubbling casseroles, oven-fresh breads, creamy soups and even sweet desserts! Believe it or not, you can savor all of the scrumptious foods you love...and still keep diabetes in check.

Simply page through *Taste of Home Diabetic Cookbook 2008,* and see what we mean. Not only does it feature 218 of the mouthwatering dishes families crave, but each recipe can be enjoyed by everyone at the table—whether they are following a special diet or not.

Even though this is the fifth edition in our popular and helpful series of books,

we're happy to say that it's still chock-full of delicious recipes made from ingredients you likely have on hand. Best of all, these dishes will help you keep healthy-eating goals without skimping on flavor, so you can eat what you like and still feel great.

In addition to nutritious main courses, savory side dishes and delectable desserts, you'll find eye-opening morning mainstays and fun finger foods perfect for entertaining. See the "Soups & Sandwiches" chapter for no-fuss lunch ideas that are sure to brighten afternoons and keep you satisfied.

Recipes that are particularly low in fat, sodium or carbohydrates are marked with quick-glance symbols. High-fiber and meatless dishes are highlighted, too. Need to set dinner on the table in half an hour? Cooking for two? Fast-to-fix dishes and tasty recipes made to serve one or two are also marked as such. For a guide to all of the colorful symbols used in this book, just refer to page 7.

Between the bright icons, easy-to-use indexes, gorgeous color photos and wide variety of foods, *Taste of Home Diabetic Cookbook 2008* makes it easier than ever to serve everyone in your family memorable meals.

Peggy Woodward, RD

KEEPING DIABETES IN CHECK

There's no quick fix to managing diabetes, but if you take these precautions, you'll be off to a good start:

WATCH THE TOTAL GRAMS OF CARBOHYDRATES IN MEALS AND SNACKS

Eat about the same amount of carbohydrates around the same time each day to help maintain an even blood sugar without spikes and valleys. The diabetic exchange system or carbohydrate counting can help you with this.

MONITOR BLOOD GLUCOSE

Check your blood glucose (sugar) regularly. Use these readings as a tool to help avoid high or low blood sugars. They will also help you learn how certain foods affect your blood glucose. A particular food can affect people very differently. Share your daily blood glucose log with your healthcare team. This will help them tailor your medications and meal plan to keep your blood glucose under control.

GET PLENTY OF EXERCISE

Exercise to shed extra pounds if you need to lose weight, because even a small weight loss can lead to improved glucose control. Regular exercise can also help decrease your risk for heart disease and stroke, improve blood circulation, decrease blood pressure and cholesterol, relieve stress and give you a lot more energy.

MAINTAIN REGULAR APPOINTMENTS WITH YOUR DIABETES CARE TEAM

Your primary diabetes doctor can help build a team of healthcare professionals that specialize in many areas of diabetes care. Your diabetes care team may include a certified diabetes educator, registered dietitian, nurse educator, eye doctor, podiatrist, dentist and an exercise physiologist. Keep regular appointments to help avoid diabetes-related complications.

ADDITIONAL RESOURCES

If you have not met with a diabetes educator or attended a diabetes education class, ask your doctor or healthcare provider about educational opportunities. A registered dietitian can help you make good food choices and also help you understand your personal meal plan.

For general information about diabetes, visit the American Diabetes Association's Web site at **www.diabetes.org** or call 1-800-DIABETES (1-800-342-2383).

To locate a diabetes educator in your area, contact the American Association of Diabetes Educators at **www.aadenet.org.**

The American Dietetic Association can provide customized answers to your nutrition questions. Visit their Web site at **www.eatright.org** or call 1-800-877-1600.

The Diabetic Newsletter, which is published every other Monday, can be sent directly to your e-mail address. The newsletter contains general information, recipes and frequently asked questions with answers. To subscribe, visit **www.diabeticnewsletter.com.**

EATING HEALTHFULLY AT YOUR FAVORITE ETHNIC RESTAURANT

Here are some smarter choices for people with diabetes to keep in mind:

ITALIAN

● Order thin-crust pizzas with veggie toppings and half the cheese of regular pizzas.

● Choose pasta dishes with tomato sauce instead of Alfredo or butter sauces.

● Order a side of steamed fresh vegetables with pasta dishes. Replace some of the carbohydrate-heavy pasta with the low-carb vegetables packed full of healthy nutrients.

● Keep portion size in mind when eating pasta—1/3 cup cooked pasta is 1 starch exchange.

● Start your meal with a vegetable salad (without cheese or croutons) instead of bread and butter. Ask for the dressing to be served on the side.

MEXICAN

● Avoid the temptation of chips and salsa altogether—ask your server to remove them from the table.

● Opt for soft chicken tacos or fajitas instead of entrées served in crisp taco shells.

● Splurge on extra lettuce and salsa.

● Steer clear of deep-fried entrées like flautas, chimichangas, chalupas and chiles rellenos.

ASIAN

● Choose entrées that feature vegetables instead of meat or noodles.

● Skip sweet and sour dishes or "fried rice" entrées.

● Leave most of the sauce in the serving dish or on your plate.

● Look for items that have been stir-fried or steamed.

● Avoid entrées that are described as battered or crispy.

HEART SMART

Heart health is especially important for people with diabetes because diabetes increases a person's risk for heart disease and stroke. Follow the tips below for heart-healthy meals any time:

FIGHT HIGH BLOOD PRESSURE

As many as two thirds of adults with diabetes also have high blood pressure. For many people, especially those with diabetes, eating salty foods may lead to high blood pressure. Here are a few ways to limit your salt intake:

● Cut back on high-sodium foods such as frozen dinners, boxed mixes, canned foods, salad dressings, soy sauce, lunch meat, sausage, processed cheese, seasoning packets, chips and pretzels.

● Use flavorful herbs and spices or salt-free seasoning blends instead of salt.

KEEP AN EYE ON CHOLESTEROL AND TRIGLYCERIDES

Research has shown that most people with diabetes have at least one lipid abnormality, such as high LDL (bad cholesterol), low HDL (good cholesterol) or high triglycerides. To keep your numbers on target:

● Avoid saturated fats (found in bacon, butter, chocolate, coconut, poultry skin, high-fat dairy products, high-fat meat, meat drippings and lard).

● Decrease trans fats (common in stick margarine, shortening and packaged products like crackers, cookies and pastries made with hydrogenated or partially hydrogenated oil).

● Choose healthy fats (found in olive and canola oils).

● Limit high-cholesterol foods (such as egg yolks, high-fat dairy products and high-fat meat products).

● Go for high-fiber foods (like oatmeal, dried beans, lentils, whole wheat bread, fruits and vegetables).

● Substitute fish high in omega-3 fatty acids for meat that is high in saturated fat. Try salmon, lake trout and albacore tuna.

Q & A

What is "pre-diabetes" and how is it different from regular diabetes?

"Pre-diabetes," which is typically a precursor to Type 2 diabetes, basically means that you have blood glucose (sugar) levels that are higher than normal but not high enough to be diagnosed with diabetes. Diabetes occurs when your body can't use the glucose flowing through your bloodstream after you eat.

Normally, your pancreas makes the hormone insulin to help your body's cells take in glucose and use it for energy. If your pancreas doesn't make enough insulin, or if your body has developed insulin resistance and can't use the insulin it's produced, there will be too much glucose in your bloodstream.

To prevent or delay pre-diabetes from becoming diabetes, aim for 30 minutes of physical activity each day and a modest weight loss if you are overweight.

What is a "free food" in the Exchange System of meal planning?

A free food for a person with diabetes is any food or drink that contains less than or equal to 20 calories and 5 grams of carbohydrate per serving. People with diabetes should not eat more than 3 free foods a day, and those should be spread throughout the day to prevent a rise in blood sugar.

Why does a food label that says "no added sugar" still have several grams of sugar listed on the Nutrition Facts panel?

"No added sugar" means that no sugars were added during processing. All kinds of foods—fruit, vegetables, milk and grains—contain natural sugar. That's why the Nutrition Facts panel would still list several grams of sugar in a "no added sugar" product. Keep in mind that the natural sugars from, for example, canned pineapple packed in its own juice also provide you with nutritious vitamins and minerals, as opposed to sugary snack foods that may only provide empty calories.

HOW WE CALCULATE NUTRITIONAL ANALYSES

- When a choice of ingredients is given in a recipe (such as 1/3 cup of sour cream or plain yogurt), the first ingredient listed was the one used for calculating the Nutrients per Serving.

- Recipe or plate garnishes were not included in our calculations.

- Optional ingredients were not included in our calculations.

- When a range is given (such as 2 to 3 teaspoons), we calculated with the first amount listed.

- Only the amount of the marinade that is absorbed during preparation was calculated.

ABOUT THE ICONS

You will find special icons included with many recipes in tthe book. With these, you can determine at a glance which recipes fit your needs. Here is a simple explanation of the icons.

 3 grams or less per serving

 140 milligrams or less per serving

 10 grams or less per serving

Quick Recipe 30 minutes or less total preparation and cook time

 5 grams or more per serving

 includes eggs and dairy products

 recipe serves 1 or 2 people

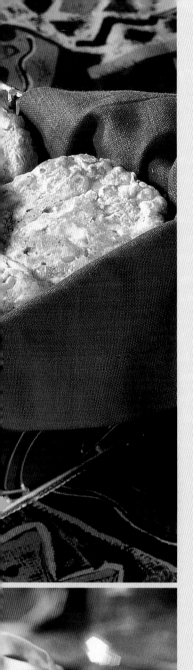

Appetizers

✌ ✌ ✌

Swimming Tuna Dip

Quick Recipe   *(Pictured at left)*

- **1 cup low-fat (1%) cottage cheese**
- **1 tablespoon reduced-fat mayonnaise**
- **1 tablespoon lemon juice**
- **2 teaspoons dry ranch-style salad dressing mix**
- **1 can (3 ounces) chunk white tuna packed in water, drained and flaked**
- **2 tablespoons sliced green onion or chopped celery**
- **1 teaspoon dried parsley flakes**
- **1 package (16 ounces) peeled baby carrots**

1. Combine cottage cheese, mayonnaise, lemon juice and salad dressing mix in food processor or blender; process until smooth.

2. Combine tuna, green onion and parsley flakes in small bowl. Stir in cottage cheese mixture. Serve with carrots.

Makes 8 servings

Nutrients per Serving: about 1/4 cup dip with 4 baby carrots

Calories 61	**Fiber** 2g
Fat 1g (sat <1g)	**Cholesterol** 6mg
Protein 6g	**Sodium** 266mg
Carbohydrate 6g	

Exchanges: 1 vegetable, 1 lean meat

Clockwise from top left: *Swimming Tuna Dip, Savory Corn Cakes (page 10), Thai Salad Rolls with Spicy Sweet & Sour Sauce (page 12) and Onion, Cheese and Tomato Tart (page 18)*

Cowboy Caviar

Quick Recipe　　　*(Pictured at right)*

Nonstick cooking spray
2 teaspoons olive oil
1 small eggplant (about 3/4 pound),
　　peeled and chopped
1 cup chopped onion
1 jalapeño pepper,* seeded and finely
　　chopped (optional)
1 can (about 15 ounces) black-eyed peas,
　　rinsed and drained
1 can (14-1/2 ounces) diced tomatoes
　　with green chiles, undrained
1 teaspoon ground cumin
1/2 cup minced fresh cilantro
Baked tortilla wedges (optional)

*Jalapeño peppers can sting and irritate the skin, so wear rubber gloves when handling peppers and do not touch your eyes.

1. Coat large nonstick skillet with cooking spray. Add oil; heat over medium heat until hot. Add eggplant, onion and jalapeño pepper, if desired; cook and stir 10 minutes or until vegetables are tender.

2. Stir in black-eyed peas, tomatoes with juice and cumin. Cook 5 minutes, stirring frequently. Remove from heat; stir in cilantro.

3. Serve with tortilla wedges, if desired.

Makes 16 servings

Nutrients per Serving: 1/4 cup dip

Calories 39	**Fiber** 1g
Fat 1g (sat <1g)	**Cholesterol** 0mg
Protein 2g	**Sodium** 184mg
Carbohydrate 7g	

Exchanges: 1-1/2 vegetable

Savory Corn Cakes

Quick Recipe　　　*(Pictured on page 8)*

2 cups all-purpose flour
1 teaspoon baking powder
1/2 teaspoon salt
2 cups frozen corn, thawed
1 cup (4 ounces) shredded smoked
　　cheddar cheese
1 cup fat-free (skim) milk
2 egg whites, beaten
1 egg, beaten
4 green onions, finely chopped
2 cloves garlic, minced
1 tablespoon chili powder
Nonstick cooking spray
Salsa (optional)

1. Combine flour, baking powder and salt in large bowl. Add corn, cheese, milk, egg whites, egg, green onions, garlic and chili powder; stir until well blended.

2. Spray large nonstick skillet with cooking spray; heat over medium-high heat.

3. Drop batter by 1/4 cupfuls into skillet; flatten to form cake. Cook 3 minutes per side or until golden brown. Serve with salsa, if desired.

Makes 12 servings

Nutrients per Serving: 1 cake

Calories 152	**Fiber** 1g
Fat 3g (sat 2g)	**Cholesterol** 25mg
Protein 6g	**Sodium** 227mg
Carbohydrate 25g	

Exchanges: 1-1/2 starch, 1/2 fat

Cowboy Caviar

Thai Salad Rolls with Spicy Sweet & Sour Sauce

(Pictured on page 8)

Spicy Sweet & Sour Sauce (recipe follows)
3 ounces thin rice noodles (rice vermicelli)
1/4 pound large raw shrimp, peeled and deveined
1 medium cucumber, peeled, seeded and cut into matchstick-size pieces
1/2 cup fresh cilantro leaves
1/2 cup fresh mint leaves
12 leaves green leaf lettuce or Boston bibb lettuce

1. Prepare Spicy Sweet & Sour Sauce; set aside. Soak noodles in hot water 10 minutes to soften. Rinse under cold running water to cool; drain.

2. Meanwhile, bring water to a boil in medium saucepan. Add shrimp; return to a boil. Cook 3 to 5 minutes or until shrimp turn pink and opaque; drain and cool slightly. Cut each shrimp lengthwise in half.

3. Arrange shrimp, noodles, cucumber, cilantro and mint in center of lettuce leaves and roll up. Serve with sauce.   *Makes 6 servings*

Spicy Sweet & Sour Sauce

1 green onion
2 tablespoons rice vinegar
1 tablespoon cornstarch
3/4 cup water
1/4 cup packed brown sugar
1/2 teaspoon red pepper flakes
2 tablespoons finely grated turnip

1. Finely chop white part of green onion; cut green portion into thin, 1-inch-long strips. Reserve green strips for garnish.

2. Combine vinegar and cornstarch in small bowl; mix well. Set aside.

3. Combine water, brown sugar, red pepper flakes and chopped green onion in small saucepan; bring to a boil. Stir in cornstarch mixture. Return to a boil; cook 1 minute or until sauce is clear and thickened. Cool. Sprinkle with turnip and reserved green onion strips just before serving.

Nutrients per Serving: 2 rolls with 2 tablespoons sauce

Calories 122	**Fiber** <1g
Fat <1g (sat <1g)	**Cholesterol** 37mg
Protein 5g	**Sodium** 54mg
Carbohydrate 25g	

Exchanges: 1-1/2 starch, 1/2 lean meat

Snackin' Cinnamon Popcorn

Quick Recipe

1 tablespoon brown sugar substitute*
1-1/2 teaspoons salt
1-1/2 teaspoons cinnamon
8 cups hot air-popped popcorn
Butter-flavored cooking spray

This recipe was tested with sucralose-based sugar substitute.

1. Combine brown sugar substitute, salt and cinnamon in small bowl; mix well.

2. Spread hot popped popcorn onto 15×10×1-inch jelly-roll pan. Coat popcorn with cooking spray; immediately sprinkle cinnamon mixture over top.

3. Serve immediately or store in airtight container.   *Makes 4 servings*

Nutrients per Serving: 2 cups popcorn

Calories 63	**Fiber** 3g
Fat 1g (sat <1g)	**Cholesterol** 0mg
Protein 2g	**Sodium** 873mg
Carbohydrate 13g	

Exchanges: 1 starch

Waldorf Appetizer Pizzas

meatless

Quick Recipe   (Pictured at bottom right)

- **1/2 large red apple, cored**
- **1 tablespoon lemon juice**
- **1 tablespoon water**
- **Nonstick cooking spray**
- **1/4 cup (1 ounce) chopped walnuts**
- **2 tablespoons golden raisins**
- **2 cloves garlic, minced**
- **3 cups packed torn stemmed spinach**
- **1 teaspoon olive oil**
- **2 packages (10 ounces each) 8-inch prepared pizza crusts**
- **1/4 cup crumbled Gorgonzola cheese or blue cheese**
- **Black pepper (optional)**

1. Preheat oven to 450°F. Thinly slice apple; cut slices into 1/2-inch pieces. Place in small bowl with lemon juice and water; stir to completely coat apple pieces. Drain; set aside.

2. Spray large skillet with cooking spray. Heat over medium-high heat until hot. Add walnuts; cook and stir 5 to 6 minutes or until nuts are light golden. Stir in apple, raisins and garlic. Add spinach and drizzle with oil. Cover; cook 1 minute or until spinach begins to wilt. Stir until spinach is just wilted and coated with oil.

3. Place pizza crusts on baking sheet. Divide spinach mixture evenly between crusts, leaving 1/2-inch border. Crumble cheese over spinach. Season with pepper, if desired. Bake 6 minutes or until cheese is melted and crusts are warm. Cut each pizza into 4 wedges.

Makes 8 servings

Nutrients per Serving: 1 pizza wedge (1/4 of 1 pizza)

Calories 267	**Fiber** 2g
Fat 8g (sat 2g)	**Cholesterol** 5mg
Protein 9g	**Sodium** 459mg
Carbohydrate 40g	

Exchanges: 2 starch, 1/2 fruit, 1/2 vegetable, 1/2 lean meat, 1 fat

S'More Gorp

low fat   low sodium   meatless

- **2 cups honey graham cereal**
- **2 cups low-fat granola cereal**
- **2 cups multi-grain cereal squares**
- **2 tablespoons butter**
- **1 tablespoon honey**
- **1/4 teaspoon ground cinnamon**
- **3/4 cup miniature marshmallows**
- **1/2 cup dried fruit bits or raisins**
- **1/4 cup mini semisweet chocolate chips**

1. Preheat oven to 275°F. Coat 15×10×1-inch jelly-roll pan with nonstick cooking spray.

2. Combine cereals in large bowl. Melt butter in small saucepan; stir in honey and cinnamon. Pour butter mixture evenly over cereal mixture; toss until cereal is well coated. Spread mixture evenly in bottom of prepared pan.

3. Bake 35 to 40 minutes or until crisp, stirring after 20 minutes. Cool completely.

4. Add marshmallows, fruit bits and chocolate chips; toss to mix. Store in airtight container.

Makes 16 servings

Nutrients per Serving: about 1/2 cup snack mix

Calories 140	**Fiber** 2g
Fat 3g (sat 2g)	**Cholesterol** 4mg
Protein 2g	**Sodium** 111mg
Carbohydrate 28g	

Exchanges: 1-1/2 starch, 1/2 fruit, 1/2 fat

Waldorf Appetizer Pizza

Christmas Confetti Dip

(Pictured at right)

1 cup fat-free sour cream
4 teaspoons dry ranch-style salad
    dressing mix
1/4 cup finely chopped seeded cucumber,
    patted dry
1/4 cup finely chopped carrot
1/4 cup finely chopped red bell pepper
1/4 cup finely chopped zucchini
    Bell pepper cutouts (optional)
    **Assorted fresh vegetables, cut up
    (optional)**

1. Combine sour cream and dressing mix
in medium bowl; mix well. Stir in chopped
cucumber, carrot, bell pepper and zucchini.
Cover; refrigerate 2 to 3 hours for flavors to
blend.

2. Transfer dip to serving bowl. Garnish with
bell pepper cutouts and serve with vegetable
dippers, if desired.   *Makes 8 servings*

Dilly of a Dip: Substitute 1/2 cup finely
chopped seeded cucumber for the 1 cup
finely chopped vegetables listed above. Stir
in 1 to 1-1/2 teaspoons dried dill weed. Makes
about 1-3/4 cups dip.

Nutrients per Serving: 1/4 cup dip (without dippers)

Calories 31	**Fiber** <1g
Fat 1g (sat <1g)	**Cholesterol** 1mg
Protein 2g	**Sodium** 37mg
Carbohydrate 4g	

Exchanges: 1 vegetable

Mini Burgers

Quick Recipe

    1 pound lean ground chicken
1/4 cup seasoned dry bread crumbs
1/4 cup chili sauce
    1 egg white
    1 tablespoon Worcestershire sauce for
    chicken
    2 teaspoons Dijon mustard
1/2 teaspoon dried thyme
1/4 teaspoon garlic powder
   32 thin slices plum tomatoes (about
    3 medium)
   16 thin sweet onion slices (about 1 small)
   16 slices cocktail rye or pumpernickel
    bread
    Mustard (optional)
    Pickle slices (optional)
    **Snipped chives or green onion tops
    (optional)**

1. Preheat oven to 350°F. Coat 15×10×1-inch
jelly-roll pan with nonstick cooking spray.
Combine chicken, bread crumbs, chili sauce,
egg white, Worcestershire sauce, mustard,
thyme and garlic powder in medium bowl.
Shape mixture into 16 patties.

2. Place patties in prepared pan. Bake,
uncovered, 10 to 15 minutes or until patties
are no longer pink in centers.

3. Place 2 tomato slices and 1 onion slice on
each bread slice; top with 1 patty. Serve with
mustard, pickle slices and chives, if desired.
    Makes 16 servings

Nutrients per Serving: 1 mini burger

Calories 74	**Fiber** 1g
Fat 2g (sat 1g)	**Cholesterol** 14mg
Protein 6g	**Sodium** 149mg
Carbohydrate 7g	

Exchanges: 1/2 starch, 1/2 lean meat

Christmas Confetti Dip

Egg Rolls

Sweet and Sour Sauce (recipe follows)
Nonstick cooking spray
3 green onions, finely chopped
3 cloves garlic, finely chopped
1/2 teaspoon ground ginger
1 can (14 ounces) bean sprouts, rinsed
    and drained
1/2 pound boneless skinless chicken breasts,
    cooked and finely chopped
1/2 cup shredded carrots
2 tablespoons reduced-sodium soy sauce
1/4 teaspoon black pepper
8 egg roll wrappers
2 teaspoons canola oil

1. Prepare Sweet and Sour Sauce; set aside.

2. Spray large nonstick skillet with cooking spray; heat over medium-high heat until hot. Add onions, garlic and ginger; cook and stir 1 minute. Add bean sprouts, chicken and carrots; cook and stir 2 minutes. Stir in soy sauce and pepper; cook and stir 1 minute. Remove skillet from heat. Let mixture stand 10 minutes or until cool enough to handle.

3. Brush edges of egg roll wrappers with water. Spoon filling evenly down centers of wrappers. Fold ends over filling; roll up.

4. Heat oil in another large nonstick skillet over medium heat until hot. Add rolls. Cook 3 to 5 minutes or until golden brown, turning occasionally. Serve hot with Sweet and Sour Sauce.   *Makes 8 servings*

Sweet and Sour Sauce

1 tablespoon plus 1 teaspoon cornstarch
1 cup water
1/2 cup sugar
1/2 cup white vinegar
1/4 cup tomato paste

Combine all ingredients in small saucepan. Bring to a boil over high heat, stirring constantly. Boil 1 minute, stirring constantly. Cool.   *Makes 8 servings (about 1-1/2 cups)*

Nutrients per Serving: 1 egg roll with about
3 tablespoons sauce

Calories 176	**Fiber** 2g
Fat 2g (sat 1g)	**Cholesterol** 19mg
Protein 10g	**Sodium** 272mg
Carbohydrate 31g	

Exchanges: 2 starch, 1/2 lean meat

ೊ ೊ ೊ

California Roll-Ups

1 cup reduced-fat ricotta cheese
2 (10-inch) flour tortillas
1 medium tomato, thinly sliced
2 cups packed torn stemmed spinach
    leaves
1 cup chopped onions
1 cup thinly sliced red or green bell
    pepper (about 1 medium)
1/2 teaspoon dried oregano
1/2 teaspoon dried basil
1/4 pounds thinly sliced cooked turkey
    breast

1. Spread 1/2 cup cheese evenly over each tortilla to within 1/4 inch of edges. Layer tomato, spinach, onions, bell pepper, oregano, basil and turkey over cheese. Roll up tortillas. Wrap in plastic wrap; refrigerate 1 hour.

2. Cut each rolled tortilla crosswise into 10 slices before serving.   *Makes 10 servings*

Nutrients per Serving: 2 roll-ups

Calories 105	**Fiber** 2g
Fat 2g (sat 1g)	**Cholesterol** 11mg
Protein 7g	**Sodium** 266mg
Carbohydrate 14g	

Exchanges: 1/2 starch, 1 vegetable, 1/2 lean meat

Mini Cheese Burritos

meatless

Quick Recipe   *(Pictured below)*

1/2 cup canned fat-free vegetarian refried beans

4 (8-inch) fat-free flour tortillas, halved

1/2 cup chunky salsa

8 sticks (1 ounce each) reduced-fat cheddar cheese*

*Reduced-fat cheddar cheese block can be substituted. Cut cheese into 2×1/4×1/4-inch sticks.

Microwave Directions

1. Spread 1 tablespoon beans over each tortilla half to within 1/2 inch of edge. Spread 1 tablespoon salsa over beans.

2. Place cheese stick on one side of each tortilla. Fold one edge of each tortilla over cheese stick; roll up. Place burritos, seam side down, on microwavable dish.

3. Microwave on HIGH 1 to 2 minutes or until cheese is melted. Let stand 1 to 2 minutes before serving.   *Makes 8 servings*

Note: This recipe was tested in an 1100-watt microwave oven.

Nutrients per Serving: 1 mini burrito

Calories 174	**Fiber** 2g
Fat 7g (sat 4g)	**Cholesterol** 16mg
Protein 10g	**Sodium** 536mg
Carbohydrate 16g	

Exchanges: 1 starch, 1 lean meat, 1 fat

Mini Cheese Burritos

Onion, Cheese and Tomato Tart

meatless

(Pictured on page 8)

Parmesan-Pepper Dough (recipe follows)
1 tablespoon butter
1 medium onion, thinly sliced
1 cup (4 ounces) shredded reduced-fat Swiss cheese
2 to 3 ripe tomatoes, sliced
Black pepper
2 tablespoons chopped fresh chives

1. Prepare Parmesan-Pepper Dough. Spray 9-inch tart pan with removable bottom with nonstick cooking spray. Press dough into bottom and up side of prepared pan.

2. Melt butter in large skillet over medium heat. Add onion; cook and stir 20 minutes.

3. Spread onion over prepared dough. Sprinkle with cheese. Let rise in warm place 20 to 30 minutes or until edges are puffy.

4. Preheat oven to 400°F. Top dough with tomatoes. Sprinkle with pepper. Bake 25 minutes or until edges are deep golden and cheese is melted. Let cool 10 minutes. Transfer to serving platter. Sprinkle with chives. Cut into wedges.   *Makes 8 servings*

Parmesan-Pepper Dough

1 package (1/4 ounce) active dry yeast
1 tablespoon sugar
2/3 cup warm water (105° to 115°F)
2 cups all-purpose flour, divided
1/4 cup grated Parmesan cheese
1 teaspoon salt
1/2 teaspoon black pepper
1 tablespoon olive oil

1. Sprinkle yeast and sugar over warm water in small bowl; stir until yeast is dissolved. Let stand 5 minutes or until mixture is bubbly.

2. Combine 1-3/4 cups flour, cheese, salt and pepper in large bowl. Pour yeast mixture and oil over flour mixture and stir until mixture clings together.

3. Spray large bowl with nonstick cooking spray. Turn out dough onto lightly floured surface. Knead 8 to 10 minutes or until smooth and elastic, adding remaining 1/4 cup flour if necessary. Shape dough into a ball. Place dough in prepared bowl, turning to coat top. Cover; let rise in warm, draft-free place 1 hour or until doubled.

4. Punch down dough. Knead on lightly floured surface 1 minute or until smooth. Flatten into a disc. Roll dough into 11-inch circle.

Nutrients per Serving: 1 tart wedge (1/8 of total recipe)

Calories 228	**Fiber** 2g
Fat 8g (sat 5g)	**Cholesterol** 19mg
Protein 9g	**Sodium** 394mg
Carbohydrate 29g	

Exchanges: 1-1/2 starch, 1-1/2 vegetable, 1/2 lean meat, 1 fat

Tip

The most important step in making successful yeast breads is dissolving the yeast properly. Dissolve the yeast with sugar in warm water. The warmth and sugar cause the yeast to grow and multiply. After about five minutes, the yeast should start to foam and bubble. If it doesn't, start over. The yeast may no longer be active. Use a thermometer to check the temperature of the water. If the water is too hot, it will kill the yeast; if it is too cool, the yeast will not activate.

Marinated Antipasto

 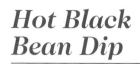 

6 cups water, divided
1 cup matchstick-size carrots
1 cup fresh green beans, cut into 2-inch pieces
1 cup fresh brussels sprouts, quartered
1 cup thinly sliced baby yellow squash
1/2 cup thinly sliced red bell pepper
1/2 cup thinly sliced yellow bell pepper
1 can (6 ounces) petite artichoke hearts, drained and quartered
1/2 cup white wine vinegar
1 tablespoon olive oil
1 teaspoon sugar
2 bay leaves
1 clove garlic
6 fresh thyme sprigs
1/4 teaspoon black pepper
1/2 cup chopped green onions
1/2 cup minced fresh parsley
Peel of 2 oranges, cut into thin strips

1. Bring 4 cups water to a boil in large saucepan over high heat. Add carrots, beans and brussels sprouts; cover and simmer 1 minute. Add squash and bell peppers; cover and simmer 1 minute or until vegetables are crisp-tender. Remove from heat; drain. Place vegetables and artichoke hearts in large heatproof bowl.

2. Combine remaining 2 cups water, vinegar, oil, sugar, bay leaves, garlic, thyme and black pepper in medium saucepan. Bring to a boil over medium heat. Pour over vegetables; mix well. Cool completely. Cover; refrigerate 12 hours or up to 3 days before serving.

3. Drain vegetables before serving; discard bay leaves, garlic and thyme. Toss vegetables with green onions, parsley and orange peel.

Makes 8 servings

Nutrients per Serving: 3/4 cup antipasto

Calories 61	**Fiber** 4g
Fat 1g (sat 0g)	**Cholesterol** 0mg
Protein 3g	**Sodium** 43mg
Carbohydrate 13g	

Exchanges: 2-1/2 vegetable

Hot Black Bean Dip

Quick Recipe   *(Pictured below)*

1 can (about 15 ounces) black beans, rinsed and drained
1 can (14-1/2 ounces) whole tomatoes, drained and chopped
1/2 to 1 canned chipotle pepper in adobo sauce, drained and minced*
1 teaspoon dried oregano leaves
1 cup (4 ounces) shredded reduced-fat Cheddar cheese
Tortilla chips (optional)

Chipotle peppers can sting and irritate the skin so wear rubber gloves when handling and do not touch your eyes.

1. Place beans in medium bowl; mash with fork or potato masher until smooth.

2. Place beans in small heavy saucepan. Stir in tomatoes, chipotle and oregano. Cook over medium heat, stirring occasionally, 5 minutes or until heated through.

3. Remove saucepan from heat. Add cheese; stir constantly until cheese melts. Transfer bean dip to serving bowl. Serve hot with tortilla chips, if desired.

Makes 8 servings

Nutrients per Serving: 1/4 cup plus 2 tablespoons dip

Calories 92	**Fiber** 4g
Fat 3g (sat 1g)	**Cholesterol** 8mg
Protein 8g	**Sodium** 458mg
Carbohydrate 13g	

Exchanges: 1/2 starch, 1 vegetable, 1/2 fat

Hot Black Bean Dip

Fresh Tomato Eggplant Spread

(Pictured at right)

1 medium eggplant
2 large ripe tomatoes, seeded and chopped
1 cup finely chopped zucchini
1/4 cup chopped green onions
2 tablespoons red wine vinegar
1 tablespoon olive oil
1 tablespoon finely chopped fresh basil
1 clove garlic, minced
2 teaspoons finely chopped fresh oregano
1 teaspoon finely chopped fresh thyme
1 teaspoon honey
1/8 teaspoon black pepper
1/4 cup pine nuts or slivered almonds
32 melba toast rounds

1. Preheat oven to 375°F. Prick eggplant all over with fork. Place in shallow baking pan. Bake 20 to 25 minutes or until tender. Cool completely. Peel and discard skin; finely chop eggplant. Place in colander; press to squeeze out excess liquid.

2. Combine eggplant, tomatoes, zucchini, green onions, vinegar, oil, basil, garlic, oregano, thyme, honey and pepper in large bowl; mix well. Cover; refrigerate 2 hours to allow flavors to blend.

3. Stir in pine nuts just before serving. Serve with melba toast rounds.   *Makes 8 servings*

Nutrients per Serving: 1/2 cup spread with 4 melba toast rounds

Calories 117	**Fiber** 2g
Fat 4g (sat 0g)	**Cholesterol** 0mg
Protein 4g	**Sodium** 65mg
Carbohydrate 15g	

Exchanges: 1/2 starch, 1-1/2 vegetable, 1/2 fat

Hummus

Quick Recipe

1 can (about 15 ounces) chickpeas, rinsed and drained
3 tablespoons lemon juice
4-1/2 teaspoons tahini*
1/2 teaspoon ground cumin
1/4 teaspoon salt
1/4 teaspoon black pepper
1/2 cup chopped seeded tomato
1/3 cup chopped red onion
1/3 cup chopped celery
1/3 cup chopped seeded cucumber
1/3 cup chopped green or red bell pepper
2 (6-inch) pita bread rounds

*Tahini, a thick paste made from ground sesame seeds, is available in the ethnic section of large supermarkets.

1. Combine chickpeas, lemon juice, tahini, cumin, salt and black pepper in food processor or blender; process until smooth. If mixture is too thick to spread, add water until desired consistency is reached.

2. Spoon chickpea mixture into serving bowl. Top with tomato, onion, celery, cucumber and bell pepper.

3. Preheat broiler. Split pita rounds to form 4 rounds. Cut each round into 6 wedges. Place on baking sheet; broil 3 minutes or until crisp.

4. Serve hummus with warm pita wedges.
Makes 6 servings

Nutrients per Serving: about 1/4 cup hummus with 4 pita wedges

Calories 188	**Fiber** 4g
Fat 4g (sat 1g)	**Cholesterol** 0mg
Protein 7g	**Sodium** 542mg
Carbohydrate 33g	

Exchanges: 2 starch, 1/2 vegetable, 1/2 fat

Fresh Tomato Eggplant Spread

Creamy Dill Veggie Dip

Quick Recipe   *(Pictured at right)*

- **4 ounces reduced-fat cream cheese**
- **2 tablespoons dry ranch-style salad dressing mix (about 1/2 package)**
- **2 tablespoons fat-free (skim) milk**
- **1 teaspoon dried dill weed *or* 1 tablespoon chopped fresh dill**
- **4 cups raw vegetables such as cherry tomatoes, celery sticks, carrots, broccoli florets, cucumber slices, and/or bell pepper strips**
- **8 plain breadsticks**

Place cream cheese, dressing mix, milk and dill weed in food processor; process until smooth. Serve dip with vegetables and breadsticks.

Makes 8 servings

Nutrients per Serving: 2 tablespoons dip with 1/2 cup vegetables and 1 breadstick

Calories 104	**Fiber** 1g
Fat 3g (sat 2g)	**Cholesterol** 8mg
Protein 3g	**Sodium** 231mg
Carbohydrate 10g	

Exchanges: 1/2 starch, 1/2 vegetable, 1/2 lean meat, 1/2 fat

ꙮ ꙮ ꙮ

Black Bean Cakes with Salsa Cruda

- **Salsa Cruda (recipe follows)**
- **1 can (about 15 ounces) black beans, rinsed and drained**
- **1/4 cup all-purpose flour**
- **1/4 cup chopped fresh cilantro**
- **2 tablespoons plain fat-free yogurt**
- **1 tablespoon chili powder**
- **2 cloves garlic, minced**
- **Nonstick cooking spray**

1. Prepare Salsa Cruda 1 hour before serving. Place beans in medium bowl; mash with fork or potato masher until chunky. Stir in flour, cilantro, yogurt, chili powder and garlic.

2. For each cake, shape 2 heaping tablespoons bean mixture into patty. Spray large nonstick skillet with cooking spray; heat over medium-high heat until hot. Cook patties 6 to 8 minutes or until lightly browned, turning once. Serve with Salsa Cruda. Garnish as desired.

Makes 4 servings

Nutrients per Serving: 2 bean cakes with 1/4 cup salsa

Calories 145	**Fiber** 8g
Fat 2g (sat <1g)	**Cholesterol** <1mg
Protein 11g	**Sodium** 415mg
Carbohydrate 30g	

Exchanges: 2 starch

Salsa Cruda

- **1 cup chopped seeded tomato**
- **2 tablespoons minced onion**
- **2 tablespoons minced fresh cilantro (optional)**
- **2 tablespoons lime juice**
- **1/2 jalapeño pepper,* seeded and minced**
- **1 clove garlic, minced**

*Jalapeño peppers can sting and irritate the skin, so wear rubber gloves when handling peppers and do not touch your eyes.

Combine all ingredients in small bowl. Refrigerate 1 hour before serving.

Makes 4 servings

Nutrients per Serving: about 1/4 cup salsa

Calories 15	**Fiber** 1g
Fat <1g (sat <1g)	**Cholesterol** 0mg
Protein <1g	**Sodium** 4mg
Carbohydrate 4g	

Exchanges: Free

Creamy Dill Veggie Dip

Fresh Fruit with Creamy Lime Dipping Sauce

Fresh Fruit with Creamy Lime Dipping Sauce

low fat   low sodium   meatless

Quick Recipe   *(Pictured above)*

1 small jicama, peeled and cut into 4×1/2-inch strips

2 tablespoons lime juice

2 pounds watermelon, rind removed, cut into 1/2-inch-thick wedges 2 to 3 inches wide

1/2 small pineapple, peeled, cored, halved lengthwise and cut crosswise into wedges

1 ripe papaya, peeled, seeded and sliced crosswise

Creamy Lime Dipping Sauce (recipe follows)

1. Combine jicama and lime juice in large bowl; toss to coat. Drain. Arrange jicama, watermelon, pineapple and papaya on large platter.

2. Serve with Creamy Lime Dipping Sauce.

Makes 8 servings

Creamy Lime Dipping Sauce

3/4 cup vanilla fat-free yogurt

2 tablespoons minced fresh cilantro

2 tablespoons lime juice

1 tablespoon minced jalapeño pepper*

*Jalapeño peppers can sting and irritate the skin, so wear rubber gloves when handling peppers and do not touch your eyes.

Combine all ingredients in small bowl; mix well.   *Makes about 3/4 cup*

Nutrients per Serving: 1/8 of fruit with about 2 tablespoons dipping sauce

Calories 98	**Fiber** 2g
Fat 1g (sat 0g)	**Cholesterol** 1mg
Protein 2g	**Sodium** 35mg
Carbohydrate 23g	

Exchanges: 1-1/2 fruit

Tip

Jicama is a root vegetable with a sweet, nutty flavor. Its crisp water chestnut-like texture makes it a perfect accompaniment to any creamy dip. It can be purchased in Mexican markets or in the produce section of most large supermarkets. Jicama is available all year, but its peak season is from November through May. Choose a firm jicama without blemishes; it should be heavy for its size with a smooth root. (Small jicamas are less fibrous.) To prepare jicama, trim off the root. Scrub the jicama with a vegetable brush under cold running water, then peel off the skin with a paring knife. If the flesh underneath the skin is very fibrous, peel off an additional layer.

Pita Pizzas

(Pictured at bottom right)

Nonstick cooking spray
1/2 pound boneless skinless chicken breasts,
 cut into 1/2-inch cubes
1/2 cup thinly sliced red bell pepper
1/2 cup thinly sliced mushrooms
1/2 cup thinly sliced red onion (about
 1 small)
2 cloves garlic, minced
1 teaspoon dried basil
1/2 teaspoon dried oregano
6 mini whole wheat pita bread rounds
1 cup packed torn stemmed spinach
 leaves
1/2 cup (2 ounces) shredded part-skim
 mozzarella cheese
1 tablespoon grated Parmesan cheese

1. Preheat oven to 375°F. Spray medium nonstick skillet with cooking spray; heat over medium heat until hot. Add chicken; cook and stir 6 minutes or until browned and no longer pink in center. Remove chicken from skillet.

2. Spray same skillet with cooking spray; add bell pepper, mushrooms, onion, garlic, basil and oregano. Cook and stir over medium heat 5 to 7 minutes or until vegetables are crisp-tender. Return chicken to skillet; stir well.

3. Place pita bread rounds on baking sheet. Top evenly with spinach and chicken mixture. Sprinkle evenly with mozzarella and Parmesan cheeses. Bake 7 to 10 minutes or until cheese is melted. *Makes 6 servings*

Nutrients per Serving: 1 pizza

Calories 158	**Fiber** 4g
Fat 3g (sat 2g)	**Cholesterol** 125mg
Protein 14g	**Sodium** 198mg
Carbohydrate 19g	

Exchanges: 1 starch, 1/2 vegetable, 1-1/2 lean meat

Savory Peanut Butter Dip

Quick Recipe

1/4 cup creamy peanut butter
3 ounces fat-free cream cheese
1 to 2 tablespoons lemon or apple juice
1/2 teaspoon ground cinnamon
1/8 to 1/4 cup natural applesauce
2 apples, sliced
1 small banana, sliced
Celery stalks, sliced into (4-inch) pieces
2 cups broccoli flowerets

Combine the peanut butter, cream cheese, juice and cinnamon in food processor. Blend until smooth. Add applesauce, little by little, to bring to the desired consistency for the dip. Chill before serving with fresh fruits or vegetables. Also try over baked sweet potatoes.

Makes 8 servings

Favorite recipe from **Peanut Advisory Board**

Nutrients per Serving: 1/4 cup dip with about 1/8 of fruits and vegetables (without sweet potato)

Calories 140	**Fiber** 4g
Fat 5g (sat 1g)	**Cholesterol** 0mg
Protein 5g	**Sodium** 240mg
Carbohydrate 18g	

Exchanges: 1 fruit, 1 vegetable, 1/2 lean meat, 1 fat

Pita Pizzas

Grilled Spiced Halibut, Pineapple and Pepper Skewers

(Pictured at right)

2 tablespoons lemon juice or lime juice

1 teaspoon minced garlic

1 teaspoon chili powder

1/2 teaspoon ground cumin

1/4 teaspoon ground cinnamon

1/8 teaspoon ground cloves

1/2 pound boneless skinless halibut steak, about 1 inch thick

1/2 small pineapple, peeled, halved lengthwise and cut into 24 pieces

1 large green or red bell pepper, cut into 24 pieces

1. Combine lemon juice, garlic, chili powder, cumin, cinnamon and cloves in large resealable food storage bag; knead until blended.

2. Rinse fish; pat dry. Cut into 12 (1- to 1-1/4-inch) cubes. Add fish to bag. Press out air; seal bag. Turn gently to coat fish with marinade. Refrigerate 30 minutes to 1 hour. Meanwhile, soak 12 (6- to 8-inch) wooden skewers in water.

3. Alternately thread 2 pieces pineapple, 2 pieces pepper and 1 piece fish onto each skewer.

4. Spray cold grill grid with nonstick cooking spray. Place grid 4 to 6 inches from heat. Preheat grill to medium-high heat. Place skewers on grill. Cover or tent with foil; grill 3 to 4 minutes or until grill marks appear on bottom. Turn skewers over; grill 3 to 4 minutes or until fish flakes when tested with fork.

Makes 6 servings

Nutrients per Serving: 2 skewers

Calories 84	**Fiber** 1g
Fat 1g (sat <1g)	**Cholesterol** 12mg
Protein 8g	**Sodium** 23mg
Carbohydrate 11g	

Exchanges: 1/2 fruit, 1 lean meat

Southwest Snack Mix

4 cups corn cereal squares

2 cups unsalted pretzels

1/2 cup unsalted pumpkin or squash seeds

1-1/2 teaspoons chili powder

1 teaspoon minced fresh cilantro or parsley

1/2 teaspoon garlic powder

1/2 teaspoon onion powder

1 egg white

2 tablespoons olive oil

2 tablespoons lime juice

1. Preheat oven to 300°F. Spray 15×10×1-inch jelly-roll pan with nonstick cooking spray.

2. Combine cereal, pretzels and pumpkin seeds in large bowl. Combine chili powder, cilantro, garlic powder and onion powder in small bowl.

3. Whisk together egg white, oil and lime juice in separate small bowl. Pour over cereal mixture; toss to coat evenly. Add seasoning mixture; mix lightly to coat evenly. Transfer to prepared pan.

4. Bake 45 minutes, stirring every 15 minutes; cool. Store in airtight container.

Makes about 12 servings

Variation: Substitute 1/2 cup unsalted peanuts for pumpkin seeds.

Nutrients per Serving: 1/2 cup snack mix

Calories 93	**Fiber** 1g
Fat 3g (sat <1g)	**Cholesterol** 0mg
Protein 2g	**Sodium** 114mg
Carbohydrate 15g	

Exchanges: 1 starch, 1/2 fat

Grilled Spiced Halibut, Pineapple and Pepper Skewers

Roasted Eggplant Spread with Focaccia

(Pictured at right)

Focaccia (recipe follows)
1 eggplant (1 pound)
1 medium tomato
1 tablespoon fresh lemon juice
1 tablespoon chopped fresh basil *or*
    1 teaspoon dried basil
2 teaspoons chopped fresh thyme *or*
    3/4 teaspoon dried thyme
1 clove garlic, minced
1/4 teaspoon salt
1 tablespoon extra-virgin olive oil
    Grape or cherry tomatoes (optional)

1. Prepare Focaccia.

2. Preheat oven to 400°F. Prick eggplant all over with fork. Place eggplant on baking sheet; bake 10 minutes. Cut stem end from tomato; place in small baking pan. Place tomato in oven with eggplant. Bake vegetables 40 minutes.

3. Cool vegetables slightly; peel. Cut eggplant into large slices. Place tomato and eggplant in food processor or blender. Add lemon juice, basil, thyme, garlic and salt; process until well blended. Slowly drizzle olive oil through processor feed tube; process until mixture is well blended. Refrigerate 3 hours or overnight.

4. To serve, spread 1 tablespoon onto each focaccia wedge. Garnish with grape or cherry tomatoes, if desired. *Makes 10 servings*

Nutrients per Serving: 3 tablespoons spread with 3 focaccia wedges

Calories 127	**Fiber** 3g
Fat 3g (sat <1g)	**Cholesterol** 0mg
Protein 4g	**Sodium** 267mg
Carbohydrate 22g	

Exchanges: 1-1/2 starch, 1/2 fat

Focaccia

3/4 cup warm water (110° to 115°F)
1-1/2 teaspoons sugar
1 teaspoon active dry yeast
1 tablespoon olive oil
1 teaspoon salt
1 teaspoon dried rosemary
1 cup all-purpose flour
1 cup whole wheat flour
    Nonstick cooking spray

1. Combine water, sugar and yeast in large bowl; stir to dissolve. Let stand 5 minutes or until bubbly. Stir in oil, salt and rosemary. Add flours, 1/2 cup at a time, stirring until dough begins to pull away from side of bowl and forms ball.

2. Spray large bowl with nonstick cooking spray. Turn out dough onto lightly floured surface; knead 5 minutes or until dough is smooth and elastic, adding more flour if necessary to prevent sticking. Shape dough into ball and place in prepared bowl, turning to coat top. Cover; let rise in warm, draft-free place about 1 hour or until doubled.

3. Spray baking sheet with cooking spray. Turn out dough onto lightly floured surface; knead 1 minute. Divide into 3 balls; roll each into 6-inch circle. Using fingertips, dimple surfaces of dough. Place on prepared baking sheet. Cover; let rise 30 minutes.

4. Preheat oven to 400°F. Spray tops of dough circles with cooking spray. Bake about 13 minutes or until golden brown. Remove from oven; cut each loaf into 10 wedges. *Makes 10 servings (30 wedges)*

Nutrients per Serving: 3 focaccia wedges

Calories 102	**Fiber** 2g
Fat 2g (sat <1g)	**Cholesterol** 0mg
Protein 3g	**Sodium** 214mg
Carbohydrate 19g	

Exchanges: 1-1/2 starch

Roasted Eggplant Spread with Focaccia

Breads

ঙ ঙ ঙ

Spiced Orange Cranberry Muffins

Quick Recipe   *(Pictured at left)*

    1/2 cup chopped fresh or frozen cranberries
      3 tablespoons packed brown sugar
      1 cup orange juice
      1 egg white
      2 tablespoons canola oil
      1 cup whole wheat flour
    1/2 cup all-purpose flour
  1-1/2 teaspoons baking powder
    1/2 teaspoon ground cinnamon
    1/4 teaspoon ground nutmeg

1. Preheat oven to 400°F. Spray 8 standard (2-1/2-inch) muffin cups with nonstick cooking spray or line with paper baking cups. Combine cranberries and brown sugar in small bowl; let stand 5 minutes. Stir in orange juice, egg white and oil.

2. Combine whole wheat flour, all-purpose flour, baking powder, cinnamon and nutmeg in medium bowl. Add cranberry mixture to flour mixture; stir just until combined. Spoon batter into prepared muffin cups.

3. Bake 18 to 20 minutes or until toothpick inserted into centers comes out clean. Immediately remove from pan; cool on wire rack. *Makes 8 servings*

Nutrients per Serving: 1 muffin

Calories 150	**Fiber** 3g
Fat 4g (sat<1g)	**Cholesterol** 0mg
Protein 4g	**Sodium** 71mg
Carbohydrate 26g	

Exchanges: 1 starch, 1/2 fruit, 1 fat

Clockwise from top left: Good-for-You Zucchini Bread (page 35), Spiced Orange Cranberry Muffins, Southwest Sausage Bread (page 39) and Tomato-Parmesan Twists (page 35)

Red Pepper Monkey Bread

(Pictured at right)

**1 package (11 ounces) refrigerated
    breadstick dough**
1/4 cup (1/2 stick) butter, melted
1/2 teaspoon dry mustard
1/2 teaspoon dried oregano
1/8 to 1/4 teaspoon garlic powder
1/4 cup sliced green onions
**1/4 cup roasted sweet red peppers, drained
    and finely chopped**

1. Preheat oven to 375°F. Coat 10-inch fluted tube pan with nonstick cooking spray. Unroll dough; separate along perforations into 12 breadsticks. Cut each breadstick into 1-inch pieces. Place half of pieces in prepared pan.

2. Combine butter, mustard, oregano and garlic powder in small bowl. Combine green onions and peppers in another small bowl. Sprinkle half of butter mixture and half of onion mixture over dough pieces in pan. Top with remaining dough pieces, butter mixture and onion mixture.

3. Bake about 25 minutes or until golden brown. Remove from pan. Serve warm.

Makes 12 servings

Nutrients per Serving: 1 piece (1/12 of bread ring)

Calories 76	**Fiber** 1g
Fat 1g (sat <1g)	**Cholesterol** 0mg
Protein 2g	**Sodium** 200mg
Carbohydrate 14g	

Exchanges: 1 starch

❧ ❧ ❧

Cloverleaf Rolls

**3/4 to 1 cup warm water (105° to 115°F),
    divided**
1 package (1/4 ounce) active dry yeast
2 teaspoons sugar
2-3/4 cups all-purpose flour
2 tablespoons canola oil
1 teaspoon salt

1. Combine 1/4 cup water, yeast and sugar in small bowl; stir until dissolved. Let stand 5 minutes or until bubbly.

2. Fit food processor with steel blade. Measure flour, oil and salt into work bowl. Process until mixed, about 15 seconds. Add yeast mixture; process until blended, about 10 seconds.

3. Turn on processor; very slowly drizzle just enough remaining water through feed tube so dough forms a ball that cleans side of bowl. Process until ball turns around bowl about 25 times. Let dough stand 1 to 2 minutes.

4. Turn on processor; gradually drizzle in enough remaining water to make dough soft, smooth and satiny but not sticky. Process until dough turns around bowl about 15 times.

5. Spray large bowl with nonstick cooking spray. Turn out dough onto lightly floured surface; shape into ball. Place in prepared bowl, turning to coat top. Cover; let rise in warm, draft-free place about 30 minutes or until almost doubled.

6. Spray 12 standard (2-1/2-inch) muffin cups with cooking spray. Punch down dough. Divide dough into 12 equal parts. Divide each part into 3 pieces. Shape each piece into a smooth ball by gently pulling top surface to underside; pinch bottom to seal. Place 3 balls in each prepared muffin cup. Cover; let rise about 1 hour or until doubled.

7. Preheat oven to 375°F. Bake rolls 15 to 20 minutes or until golden. Immediately remove from pan to wire rack. *Makes 12 servings*

Nutrients per Serving: 1 roll

Calories 129	**Fiber** 1g
Fat 3g (sat <1g)	**Cholesterol** 0mg
Protein 3g	**Sodium** 199mg
Carbohydrate 23g	

Exchanges: 1-1/2 starch, 1/2 fat

Red Pepper Monkey Bread

Pumpkin Raisin Muffin

Pumpkin Raisin Muffins

(Pictured above)

3/4 cup canned pumpkin
6 tablespoons vegetable oil
1 egg
2 egg whites
1 tablespoon light molasses
1 teaspoon vanilla
1-1/4 cups all-purpose flour
1 cup EQUAL® SPOONFUL*
1/2 cup raisins
1 tablespoon baking powder
1 teaspoon ground cinnamon
1/2 teaspoon ground nutmeg
1/2 teaspoon ground ginger
1/4 teaspoon salt

May substitute 24 packets EQUAL® sweetener.

• Combine pumpkin, oil, egg and egg whites, molasses and vanilla. Stir in combined flour, Equal®, raisins, baking powder, cinnamon, nutmeg, ginger and salt just until all ingredients are moistened. Fill paper-lined 2-1/2-inch muffin cups about 3/4 full.

• Bake in preheated 375°F oven 18 to 20 minutes or until wooden pick inserted into centers comes out clean. Cool in pan on wire rack 2 to 3 minutes. Remove muffins from pan and cool completely on wire rack.

Makes 12 muffins

Nutrients per Serving: 1 muffin

Calories 149	**Fiber** 1g
Fat 8g (sat 1g)	**Cholesterol** 18mg
Protein 3g	**Sodium** 224mg
Carbohydrate 18g	

Exchanges: 1 starch, 1-1/2 fat

Tomato-Parmesan Twists

low fat

Quick Recipe   *(Pictured on page 30)*

2 tablespoons sun-dried tomatoes (not packed in oil)

1/4 cup hot water

1 package (11 ounces) refrigerated breadstick dough

3 tablespoons finely shredded Parmesan cheese, divided

1 teaspoon olive oil

2 cloves garlic, minced

1/4 teaspoon Italian seasoning (optional)

1/4 teaspoon black pepper

1. Preheat oven to 375°F. Coat baking sheet with nonstick cooking spray or line with parchment paper.

2. Soak tomatoes in hot water 10 minutes; drain. Chop tomatoes.

3. Unroll dough; cut in half widthwise (each half will measure about 7×6 inches and contain 6 breadsticks). Sprinkle 2 tablespoons cheese over 1 dough rectangle. Sprinkle with tomatoes. Firmly press cheese and tomatoes into dough. Place remaining dough rectangle on top; press edges to seal.

4. Using serrated knife, cut filled dough in half lengthwise into 2 rectangles, each measuring 7×3 inches. Cut each half into 6 short strips along perforation lines. Twist each dough strip one time. Place on prepared baking sheet. Lightly brush each dough strip with olive oil.

5. Combine garlic, Italian seasoning, if desired, and pepper in small bowl; sprinkle over dough twists. Top with remaining 1 tablespoon cheese. Bake 11 to 13 minutes or until golden brown. Serve warm.   *Makes 12 servings*

Nutrients per Serving: 1 twist

Calories 77	**Fiber** <1g
Fat 2g (sat <1g)	**Cholesterol** 1mg
Protein 2g	**Sodium** 209mg
Carbohydrate 13g	

Exchanges: 1 starch

Good-for-You Zucchini Bread

low fat

(Pictured on page 30)

2/3 cup pitted prunes

3 tablespoons water

1 cup sugar

1/2 cup orange juice

1 teaspoon grated orange peel

2 cups grated zucchini

1-1/2 cups all-purpose flour

1-1/2 cups whole wheat flour

2 teaspoons pumpkin pie spice*

1 teaspoon baking powder

1 teaspoon baking soda

1/4 teaspoon salt

1/4 cup plain low-fat yogurt

Or, substitute 1 teaspoon ground cinnamon, 1/2 teaspoon ground ginger and 1/4 teaspoon each ground allspice and ground nutmeg for 2 teaspoons pumpkin pie spice.

1. Preheat oven to 350°F. Coat 9×5-inch loaf pan with nonstick cooking spray.

2. Combine prunes and water in food processor or blender; process until smooth. Combine prune mixture, sugar, orange juice and orange peel in large bowl; mix well. Stir in zucchini.

3. Combine flours, pumpkin pie spice, baking powder, baking soda and salt in medium bowl. Stir half of flour mixture into zucchini mixture. Stir in half of yogurt. Repeat with remaining flour mixture and yogurt; stir just until blended. Pour batter into prepared pan.

4. Bake 1 hour and 15 minutes or until toothpick inserted into center comes out clean. Cool in pan on wire rack 10 minutes. Remove from pan; cool completely.

Makes 16 servings

Nutrients per Serving: 1 slice (1/16 of total recipe)

Calories 157	**Fiber** 2g
Fat <1g (sat <1g)	**Cholesterol** <1mg
Protein 3g	**Sodium** 147mg
Carbohydrate 36g	

Exchanges: 1-1/2 starch, 1 fruit, 1/2 vegetable

Berry Bran Muffins

(Pictured at right)

2 cups dry bran cereal
1-1/4 cups fat-free (skim) milk
1/2 cup packed brown sugar
1/4 cup canola oil
1 egg, lightly beaten
1 teaspoon vanilla extract
1-1/4 cups all-purpose flour
1 tablespoon baking powder
1/4 teaspoon salt
1 cup fresh or frozen blueberries

1. Preheat oven to 350°F. Spray 12 standard (2-1/2-inch) muffin cups with nonstick cooking spray.

2. Mix cereal and milk in medium bowl; let stand 5 minutes to soften. Beat in brown sugar, oil, egg and vanilla. Combine flour, baking powder and salt in large bowl. Stir in cereal mixture just until dry ingredients are moistened. Gently fold in berries. Spoon batter into prepared muffin cups.

3. Bake 20 to 25 minutes or until toothpick inserted into centers comes out clean. Remove from pan to wire rack.   *Makes 12 servings*

Nutrients per Serving: 1 muffin

Calories 172	**Fiber** 4g
Fat 5g (sat 1g)	**Cholesterol** 18mg
Protein 4g	**Sodium** 287mg
Carbohydrate 29g	

Exchanges: 2 starch, 1 fat

ஃ ஃ ஃ

Crusty Water Rolls

low fat

1/4 to 1/2 cup warm water (105° to 115°F), divided
1 package (1/4 ounce) active dry yeast
1 teaspoon sugar
3/4 teaspoon salt
2 egg whites
2-1/4 cups all-purpose flour
2 tablespoons canola oil
2 tablespoons cornmeal

1. Combine 1/4 cup water, yeast, sugar and salt in small bowl; stir to dissolve. Let stand 5 minutes or until bubbly. Blend in egg whites.

2. Fit food processor with steel blade. Measure flour and oil into work bowl. Process until mixed, about 10 seconds. Turn on processor; very slowly drizzle yeast mixture through feed tube. Process until blended, about 10 seconds.

3. Turn on processor; very slowly drizzle in just enough remaining water so dough forms a ball that cleans side of bowl. Process until ball turns around bowl about 25 times. Let dough stand 1 to 2 minutes.

4. Turn on processor; gradually drizzle in enough remaining water to make dough soft, smooth and satiny but not sticky. Process until dough turns around bowl about 15 times.

5. Spray large bowl with nonstick cooking spray. Turn out dough onto lightly floured surface; shape into ball. Place in prepared bowl, turning to coat top. Cover; let rise in warm, draft-free place about 1 hour or until doubled.

6. Spray baking sheet with cooking spray. Punch down dough. Cover; let rest 10 minutes. Divide dough into 9 pieces. Shape each piece into a smooth ball by gently pulling top surface to underside; pinch bottom to seal. Dip bottom side in cornmeal. Place dough balls on prepared baking sheet about 1-1/2 inches apart. Cover; let rise about 1 hour or until doubled.

7. Place shallow pan of water on bottom rack of oven. Preheat oven to 400°F. Brush rolls with cold water. Bake 15 to 18 minutes or until golden. Brush or spray rolls with cold water once or twice during baking, if desired, for crisper crusts. Immediately remove from baking sheet to wire rack.   *Makes 9 servings*

Nutrients per Serving: 1 roll

Calories 157	**Fiber** 1g
Fat 3g (sat <1g)	**Cholesterol** 0mg
Protein 4g	**Sodium** 211mg
Carbohydrate 27g	

Exchanges: 2 starch, 1/2 fat

Berry Bran Muffins

Olive Twists

Breadsticks

Breadsticks
> **1-1/4 cups water (70° to 80°F)**
> > **1 teaspoon salt**
> > **1 teaspoon sugar**
> > **1 tablespoon olive oil**
> > **3 cups bread flour**
> > **1 tablespoon rapid-rise active dry yeast**

Toppings
> > **2 to 3 tablespoons olive oil**
> **1-1/2 to 2 tablespoons poppy seeds, sesame seeds or coarse salt**

Bread Machine Directions

1. Measuring carefully, place all ingredients except toppings in bread machine pan in order specified by owner's manual. Program dough cycle setting; press start.

2. Coat two baking sheets with nonstick cooking spray. Turn out dough onto lightly floured surface. Shape dough into smooth ball. Cut dough into 12 pieces. Roll each piece into 16-inch rope; twist ropes and place on prepared baking sheets.

3. Brush breadsticks with 2 to 3 tablespoons oil. Spread poppy seeds on large plate. Roll breadsticks, one at a time, in poppy seeds; return to prepared baking sheets.

4. Preheat oven to 350°F. (Breadsticks will rise slightly while oven preheats.) Bake 30 to 35 minutes or until golden brown and crispy.
Makes 12 breadsticks

Nutrients per Serving: 1 breadstick (1/12 of total recipe)

Calories 165	**Fiber** 1g
Fat 5g (sat 1g)	**Cholesterol** 0mg
Protein 5g	**Sodium** 198mg
Carbohydrate 26g	

Exchanges: 1-1/2 starch, 1 fat

Olive Twists

Quick Recipe   (Pictured at top left)

> **1 package (11 ounces) refrigerated breadstick dough**
> **1 egg white, beaten**
> > **Paprika**
> **12 pimiento-stuffed green olives, chopped**

1. Preheat oven to 375°F. Line baking sheet with parchment paper. Unroll dough; separate into 12 pieces along perforation lines.

2. Brush dough lightly with egg white. Sprinkle with paprika and chopped green olives. Twist each stick 3 or 4 times. Bake 11 to 13 minutes or until golden brown.   *Makes 12 servings*

Nutrients per Serving: 1 twist

Calories 79	**Fiber** <1g
Fat 2g (sat <1g)	**Cholesterol** 0mg
Protein 2g	**Sodium** 280mg
Carbohydrate 12g	

Exchanges: 1 starch

Southwest Sausage Bread

(Pictured on page 30)

1 package (1/4 ounce) active dry yeast
1 tablespoon sugar
1 cup warm water (105° to 115°F)
2 to 2-1/4 cups all-purpose flour, divided
1-1/2 cups whole wheat flour, divided
1 egg
2 tablespoons canola oil
1/4 teaspoon salt
1 medium onion, finely chopped
1/4 pound chorizo* or pepperoni sausage, chopped
1 cup (4 ounces) shredded Monterey Jack cheese

Chorizo is a highly seasoned Mexican pork sausage.

1. Sprinkle yeast and sugar over warm water in large bowl; stir until dissolved. Let stand 5 minutes or until bubbly. Add 1 cup all-purpose flour, 1 cup whole wheat flour, egg, oil and salt. Beat until blended. Beat 3 minutes. Stir in remaining whole-wheat flour and enough all-purpose flour, about 3/4 cup, to make soft dough.

2. Spray large bowl with nonstick cooking spray. Sprinkle work surface with all-purpose flour. Turn out dough onto prepared surface; flatten. Knead 5 to 8 minutes or until smooth and elastic; gradually add remaining 1/2 cup all-purpose flour to prevent sticking, if necessary. Shape into ball; place in prepared bowl, turning to coat top. Cover; let rise in warm, draft-free place about 1 hour or until doubled.

3. Cook onion and sausage in skillet over medium heat 5 minutes or until onion is tender. Drain on paper towels.

4. Spray 9×5-inch loaf pan with nonstick cooking spray. Punch down dough. Knead on floured surface 1 minute. Cover; let rest 10 minutes. Roll dough into 24×11-inch rectangle. Sprinkle sausage mixture and cheese over dough. Roll up dough jelly-roll style from short end. Pinch seam and ends to seal. Cut dough lengthwise in half. With cut sides up, twist halves together. Pinch ends to seal. Place in prepared pan, cut sides up. Cover; let rise about 1 hour or until doubled.

5. Preheat oven to 375°F. Bake 30 minutes or until loaf sounds hollow when tapped. Remove immediately from pan. Cool 30 minutes on wire rack. Refrigerate leftovers.

Makes 12 servings

Nutrients per Serving: 1 slice (1/12 of total recipe)

Calories 232	**Fiber** 3g
Fat 10g (sat 4g)	**Cholesterol** 34mg
Protein 9g	**Sodium** 224mg
Carbohydrate 28g	

Exchanges: 2 starch, 1/2 lean meat, 1 fat

❧ ❧ ❧

Mini Blueberry-Citrus Muffins

Quick Recipe

1 package (7 ounces) blueberry muffin mix
1 egg white
4-1/2 teaspoons lemon juice
1 teaspoon grated orange peel
1/2 teaspoon grated lemon peel

1. Preheat oven to 425°F. Spray 12 mini (1-3/4-inch) nonstick muffin cups with nonstick cooking spray.

2. Combine all ingredients in medium bowl; stir until just blended. *Do not overmix.* Spoon batter into prepared muffin cups.

3. Bake 12 to 15 minutes or until toothpick inserted into centers comes out clean. Remove to wire rack; cool. *Makes 12 servings*

Nutrients per Serving: 1 mini muffin

Calories 69	**Fiber** <1g
Fat 1g (sat <1g)	**Cholesterol** 0mg
Protein 1g	**Sodium** 130mg
Carbohydrate 13g	

Exchanges: 1 starch

Cranberry Scones

(Pictured at right)

2-1/2 cups all-purpose flour
1/2 cup packed brown sugar
1 tablespoon baking powder
1 teaspoon baking soda
3/4 teaspoon salt
1/2 teaspoon ground cinnamon
1/4 cup Dried Plum Purée (page 46)
**   or prepared dried plum butter**
2 tablespoons cold margarine or butter
1 container (8 ounces) nonfat vanilla
**   yogurt**
3/4 cup dried cranberries
1 egg white, lightly beaten
1 tablespoon granulated sugar

Preheat oven to 400°F. Coat baking sheet with vegetable cooking spray. In large bowl, combine flour, brown sugar, baking powder, baking soda, salt and cinnamon. Cut in Dried Plum Purée and margarine with pastry blender until mixture resembles coarse crumbs. Mix in yogurt just until blended. Stir in cranberries. On floured surface, roll or pat dough to 3/4-inch thickness. Cut out with 2-1/2- to 3-inch biscuit cutter, rerolling scraps as needed, but handling as little as possible. Arrange on prepared baking sheet, spacing 2 inches apart. Brush with egg white and sprinkle with granulated sugar. Bake in center of oven about 15 minutes until golden brown and springy to the touch. Serve warm or at room temperature.   *Makes 12 scones*

Favorite recipe from **California Dried Plum Board**

Nutrients per Serving: 1 scone

Calories 198	**Fiber** 1g
Fat 2g (sat 2g)	**Cholesterol** <1mg
Protein 4g	**Sodium** 415mg
Carbohydrate 41g	

Exchanges: 1-1/2 starch, 1 fruit, 1/2 fat

Lemon Raisin Quick Bread

1-1/4 cups all-purpose flour
3/4 cup whole wheat flour
4 tablespoons sugar, divided
2 teaspoons baking powder
1/2 teaspoon baking soda
1/4 teaspoon salt
1-1/2 cups (12 ounces) lemon low-fat yogurt
1/4 cup (1/2 stick) unsalted butter, melted
**   and cooled slightly**
1 egg
1/2 teaspoon grated lemon peel
1 cup raisins
3/4 cup chopped walnuts (optional)

1. Preheat oven to 350°F. Spray 8-1/2×4-1/2-inch loaf pan with nonstick cooking spray.

2. Combine flours, 3 tablespoons sugar, baking powder, baking soda and salt in large bowl. Combine yogurt, butter, egg and lemon peel in medium bowl; stir until well blended. Pour yogurt mixture into flour mixture. Add raisins and walnuts, if desired; stir just until dry ingredients are moistened. Pour into prepared pan; smooth top. Sprinkle with remaining 1 tablespoon sugar.

3. Bake 40 to 45 minutes or until lightly browned and toothpick inserted into center comes out clean. Cool in pan on wire rack 15 minutes. Remove from pan; cool completely.
Makes 12 servings

Nutrients per Serving: 1 slice (1/12 of total recipe)

Calories 183	**Fiber** 2g
Fat 5g (sat 3g)	**Cholesterol** 30mg
Protein 5g	**Sodium** 198mg
Carbohydrate 31g	

Exchanges: 1-1/2 starch, 1/2 fruit, 1 fat

Tomato-Artichoke Focaccia

`low fat`

(Pictured at right)

1 package (16 ounces) hot roll mix
2 tablespoons wheat bran
1-1/4 cups hot water (120° to 130°F)
4 teaspoons olive oil, divided
1 cup thinly sliced onion
2 cloves garlic, minced
1 cup sun-dried tomatoes (4 ounces dry), rehydrated* and cut into strips
1 cup canned artichoke hearts, sliced
1 tablespoon minced fresh rosemary
2 tablespoons grated Parmesan cheese

*To rehydrate sun-dried tomatoes, pour 1 cup boiling water over tomatoes in small heatproof bowl; let soak 5 to 10 minutes or until softened. Drain well.

1. Preheat oven to 400°F. Combine dry ingredients and contents of yeast packet from hot roll mix in large bowl. Add bran; mix well. Stir in hot water and 2 teaspoons oil. Knead dough on lightly floured surface about 5 minutes or until ingredients are blended.

2. Spray 15×10×1-inch jelly-roll pan or 14-inch pizza pan with nonstick cooking spray. Press dough onto bottom of prepared pan. Cover; let rise 15 minutes.

3. Heat 1 teaspoon oil in medium skillet over low heat. Add onion and garlic; cook and stir 2 to 3 minutes or until onions are tender.

4. Brush surface of dough with remaining 1 teaspoon oil. Top dough with onion mixture, tomatoes, artichokes and fresh rosemary. Sprinkle with Parmesan.

5. Bake 25 to 30 minutes or until lightly browned on top. Cut into 16 pieces.

Makes 16 servings

Nutrients per Serving: 1 piece focaccia

Calories 152	**Fiber** 2g
Fat 3g (sat <1g)	**Cholesterol** <1mg
Protein 5g	**Sodium** 238mg
Carbohydrate 26g	

Exchanges: 1-1/2 starch, 1/2 vegetable, 1 fat

Oatmeal Pumpkin Bread

1 cup quick-cooking oats
1 cup low-fat milk, heated
3/4 cup cooked or canned pumpkin
2 eggs, beaten
1/4 cup margarine, melted
2 cups all-purpose flour
1 cup sugar
1 tablespoon baking powder
1 teaspoon ground cinnamon
1/4 teaspoon salt
1/4 teaspoon ground nutmeg
1 cup raisins
1/2 cup chopped pecans

Preheat oven to 350°F. In large bowl, combine oats and milk; let stand about 5 minutes. Stir in pumpkin, eggs and margarine. In separate bowl, mix together flour, sugar, baking powder, cinnamon, salt and nutmeg. Gradually add dry ingredients to oatmeal mixture. Stir in raisins and nuts; mix well. Place in greased 9×5-inch loaf pan. Bake 55 to 60 minutes or until done. Cool on wire rack.   *Makes 1 loaf (16 slices)*

Favorite recipe from **The Sugar Association, Inc.**

Nutrients per Serving: 1 slice (1/16 of total recipe)

Calories 227	**Fiber** 2g
Fat 7g (sat 1g)	**Cholesterol** 28mg
Protein 5g	**Sodium** 179mg
Carbohydrate 39g	

Exchanges: 2-1/2 starch, 1 fat

Tip

Store quick breads at room temperature, wrapped in plastic wrap, for up to 3 days. Or, freeze quick breads, wrapped in heavy-duty foil, for up to 3 months. To reheat frozen bread, wrap it in foil and bake at 300°F for 15 to 18 minutes.

Tomato-Artichoke Focaccia

Thyme-Cheese Bubble Loaf

Thyme-Cheese Bubble Loaf

(Pictured above)

1 package (1/4 ounce) active dry yeast
1 teaspoon sugar
1 cup warm water (105° to 115°F)
3 cups all-purpose flour
1 teaspoon salt
2 tablespoons canola oil
1 cup (4 ounces) shredded Monterey Jack
  cheese
1/4 cup (1/2 stick) butter, melted
1/4 cup chopped fresh parsley
  3 teaspoons finely chopped fresh thyme
    ***or* 3/4 teaspoon dried thyme**

1. Sprinkle yeast and sugar over warm water in small bowl; stir until dissolved. Let stand 5 minutes or until bubbly.

2. Fit food processor with steel blade. Measure flour and salt into work bowl. With processor running, add yeast mixture and oil through feed tube. Process until mixture forms dough that leaves side of bowl. If dough is too dry, add 1 to 2 tablespoons water. If dough is too wet, add 1 to 2 tablespoons additional flour until dough leaves side of bowl. Dough will be sticky.

3. Spray large bowl with nonstick cooking spray. Place dough in prepared bowl. Turn dough to coat top. Cover; let rise in warm, draft-free place about 1 hour or until doubled.

4. Punch down dough. Knead cheese into dough on lightly floured surface until evenly distributed. Cover; let rest 10 minutes.

5. Spray 1-1/2-quart casserole or 8×4-inch loaf pan with cooking spray; set aside. Combine butter, parsley and thyme in small bowl.

6. Roll out dough into 8×6-inch rectangle with lightly floured rolling pin. Cut dough into 48 (1-inch) squares. Shape into balls; dip into parsley mixture. Place in prepared dish. Cover; let rise about 45 minutes or until doubled.

7. Preheat oven to 375°F. Bake 35 to 40 minutes or until top is golden and loaf sounds hollow when tapped. Immediately remove from casserole dish; cool on wire rack 30 minutes. Serve warm.   *Makes 12 servings*

Nutrients per Serving: 4 bubbles (1/12 of loaf)

Calories 206	**Fiber** 1g
Fat 9g (sat 5g)	**Cholesterol** 18mg
Protein 6g	**Sodium** 276mg
Carbohydrate 25g	

Exchanges: 1-1/2 starch, 1/2 lean meat, 1-1/2 fat

Tip

Fresh herbs are very perishable, so purchase them in small amounts. For short-term storage, place the herb stems in water. Cover leaves loosely with a plastic bag or plastic wrap and store in the refrigerator. Thyme will last up to 5 days.

Blueberry Lemon Scones

 low fat

2-2/3 cups all-purpose flour
1/2 cup plus 2 tablespoons sugar, divided
2-1/2 teaspoons baking powder
1 teaspoon baking soda
1/2 teaspoon salt
1/2 cup dried blueberries
1 container (8 ounces) nonfat lemon yogurt
1/3 cup Dried Plum Purée (page 46) or prepared dried plum butter
3 tablespoons butter or margarine, melted
1 tablespoon grated lemon peel
2 teaspoons vanilla
1/4 teaspoon ground nutmeg

Preheat oven to 400°F. Coat baking sheet with vegetable cooking spray. In large bowl, combine flour, 1/2 cup sugar, baking powder, baking soda and salt. Add blueberries. In small bowl, mix yogurt, Dried Plum Purée, butter, lemon peel and vanilla until blended. Add to flour mixture; mix just until mixture holds together. Turn dough out onto lightly floured surface and pat into 10-inch round. Combine the remaining 2 tablespoons sugar and nutmeg; sprinkle evenly over dough. Pat sugar mixture gently into dough; cut into 12 equal wedges. Place wedges on prepared baking sheet, spacing 1 inch apart. Bake in center of oven about 15 minutes until lightly browned and cracked on top. Remove to wire rack to cool slightly.   *Makes 12 scones*

Favorite recipe from **California Dried Plum Board**

Nutrients per Serving: 1 scone

Calories 221	**Fiber** 1g
Fat 3g (sat 2g)	**Cholesterol** 8mg
Protein 4g	**Sodium** 351mg
Carbohydrate 44g	

Exchanges: 2 starch, 1 fruit, 1/2 fat

Whole Wheat Focaccia

low fat   low sodium   high fiber

3 teaspoons olive oil, divided
1 cup chopped onion
1/4 cup chopped red bell pepper
3 cloves garlic, chopped
1/2 teaspoon paprika
2 cups whole wheat flour
1/2 cup all-purpose flour, divided
1 package (1/4 ounce) rapid-rise yeast
1/2 teaspoon sugar
1/4 teaspoon salt
1 cup hot water (120° to 130°F)
2 teaspoons dried oregano
1/4 to 1/2 teaspoon black pepper

1. Heat 1 teaspoon olive oil in large nonstick skillet over medium heat. Cook and stir onion, bell pepper, garlic and paprika 5 minutes.

2. Brush 12-inch pizza pan with remaining oil. Combine whole wheat flour, 2 tablespoons all-purpose flour, yeast, sugar and salt in large bowl. Stir in water.

3. Sprinkle work surface with 1 tablespoon all-purpose flour. Turn out dough; knead 3 minutes or until smooth, adding up to 2 tablespoons all-purpose flour to prevent sticking if necessary. Cover; let rest 10 minutes. Place oven rack in lowest position; preheat oven to 425°F.

4. Knead dough on lightly floured surface about 3 minutes. Add remaining all-purpose flour as needed to make smooth and elastic dough. Roll out dough to 13-inch round; transfer to prepared pan. Crimp edge of dough to form rim.

5. Spread topping on dough; sprinkle with oregano and black pepper. Bake 15 to 20 minutes or until edge is lightly browned. Remove from pan to wire rack; cool 5 minutes. Cut into wedges.   *Makes 8 servings*

Nutrients per Serving: 1 focaccia wedge (1/8 of total recipe)

Calories 162	**Fiber** 5g
Fat 2g (sat <1g)	**Cholesterol** 0mg
Protein 6g	**Sodium** 69mg
Carbohydrate 31g	

Exchanges: 2 starch, 1/2 vegetable

Jelly Donut Muffins

(Pictured at right)

1-1/4 cups nonfat milk

1/4 cup Dried Plum Purée (recipe follows) or prepared dried plum butter

1 egg

2 tablespoons vegetable oil

1 teaspoon vanilla

2 cups all-purpose flour

1/3 cup sugar

1 tablespoon baking powder

1 teaspoon ground cardamom or cinnamon

1/2 teaspoon salt

1/4 cup strawberry jam

Preheat oven to 425°F. Coat twelve 2-3/4-inch (1/3-cup capacity) muffin cups with vegetable cooking spray. In large bowl, beat first five ingredients until well blended. In medium bowl, combine flour, sugar, baking powder, cardamom and salt. Add to milk mixture; mix just until blended. Spoon about half of batter into prepared muffin cups. Top each with 1 teaspoon jam and remaining batter, covering jam completely. Bake 15 to 20 minutes or until springy to the touch. Cool in pans 10 minutes. Remove to wire rack to cool slightly. Serve warm.   *Makes 12 muffins*

Dried Plum Purée: Combine 1-1/3 cups (8 ounces) pitted dried plums and 6 tablespoons hot water in container of food processor or blender. Pulse on and off until dried plums are finely chopped and smooth. Store leftovers in a covered container in the refrigerator for up to two months. Makes 1 cup.

Favorite recipe from **California Dried Plum Board**

Nutrients per Serving: 1 muffin

Calories 181	**Fiber** 2g
Fat 3g (sat <1g)	**Cholesterol** 18mg
Protein 4g	**Sodium** 220mg
Carbohydrate 35g	

Exchanges: 2 starch, 1/2 fruit, 1/2 fat

Applesauce Date Muffins

Quick Recipe

2/3 cup all-purpose flour

1/3 cup whole wheat flour

2 tablespoons sugar

1-1/2 teaspoons baking powder

1/2 teaspoon ground cinnamon

1/4 teaspoon salt

1/4 teaspoon ground allspice

10 whole dates, pitted and cut into 1/2-inch pieces

2/3 cup unsweetened applesauce

2 tablespoons canola oil

1 egg white, lightly beaten

1/2 teaspoon vanilla extract

1. Preheat oven to 400°F. Coat 6 standard (2-1/2-inch) muffin cups with nonstick cooking spray. Sift all-purpose flour, whole wheat flour, sugar, baking powder, cinnamon, salt and allspice into large bowl. Stir in dates until coated with flour.

2. Combine applesauce, oil, egg white and vanilla in small bowl. Make well in flour mixture. Pour applesauce mixture into well, stirring just to combine. *Do not overmix.* Spoon batter into prepared muffin cups.

3. Bake 15 minutes or until toothpick inserted into centers comes out clean. Immediately remove from pan to wire rack.

Makes 6 servings

Nutrients per Serving: 1 muffin

Calories 184	**Fiber** 3g
Fat 5g (sat <1g)	**Cholesterol** 0mg
Protein 3g	**Sodium** 182mg
Carbohydrate 33g	

Exchanges: 1 starch, 1 fruit, 1 fat

Breakfast & Brunch

৯ ৯ ৯

Blueberry-Orange French Toast Casserole

high fiber

(Pictured at left)

6 slices 100% whole wheat bread, cut into 1-inch pieces
1 cup fresh blueberries (not frozen)
1/2 cup sugar substitute*
1/2 cup fat-free (skim) milk
2 eggs
4 egg whites
1 tablespoon grated orange peel
1/2 teaspoon vanilla extract

This recipe was tested with sucralose-based sugar substitute.

1. Preheat oven to 350°F. Coat 8-inch square baking dish with nonstick cooking spray. Place bread and blueberries in dish; toss gently to combine.

2. Whisk sugar substitute into milk in medium bowl until dissolved. Whisk in eggs, egg whites, orange peel and vanilla; pour over bread mixture. Toss to coat. Let stand 5 minutes.

3. Bake 40 to 45 minutes or until top is browned and knife inserted into center comes out clean. Let stand 5 minutes before serving.   *Makes 4 servings*

Nutrients per Serving: 1 piece (1/4 of total recipe)

Calories 284	**Fiber** 5g
Fat 5g (sat 2g)	**Cholesterol** 107mg
Protein 12g	**Sodium** 309mg
Carbohydrate 50g	

Exchanges: 3 starch, 1/2 fruit, 1/2 lean meat

Clockwise from top left: *Blueberry-Orange French Toast Casserole, Pumpkin Pancakes (page 50), Fruited Granola (page 53) and Ham and Vegetable Omelet (page 60)*

y Orange

ctured at right)

...ose flour

.cup sugar

1-1/2 teaspoons baking powder

1 teaspoon salt

1/2 teaspoon baking soda

1/4 teaspoon ground cloves

1 tablespoon grated orange peel

3/4 cup orange juice

1 egg, lightly beaten

2 tablespoons canola oil

1 teaspoon vanilla extract

1/4 teaspoon orange extract

1 cup whole cranberries

1. Preheat oven to 350°F. Spray 12-cup fluted tube pan with nonstick cooking spray; set aside.

2. Combine flour, sugar, baking powder, salt, baking soda and cloves in large bowl. Add orange peel; mix well.

3. Combine orange juice, egg, oil, vanilla and orange extract in medium bowl; beat until well blended. Add orange juice mixture to flour mixture; stir until just moistened. Gently fold in cranberries. *Do not overmix.*

4. Spread batter evenly in prepared pan. Bake 30 to 35 minutes (35 to 40 minutes if using frozen cranberries) or until toothpick inserted near center comes out clean. Cool in pan on wire rack 15 to 20 minutes. Invert onto serving plate. Serve warm or at room temperature.

Makes 12 servings

Nutrients per Serving: 1 slice (1/12 of total recipe)

Calories 181	**Fiber** 1g
Fat 3g (sat <1g)	**Cholesterol** 18mg
Protein 3g	**Sodium** 314mg
Carbohydrate 36g	

Exchanges: 2 starch, 1/2 fruit

Pumpkin Pancakes

Quick Recipe *(Pictured on page 48)*

1 cup all-purpose flour

3 tablespoons sugar substitute*

1 teaspoon baking powder

1/2 teaspoon pumpkin pie spice**

1/4 teaspoon baking soda

1/4 teaspoon salt

3/4 cup low-fat buttermilk

1/2 cup solid-pack pumpkin

1 egg

1 tablespoon canola oil

1/2 teaspoon vanilla extract

Nonstick cooking spray

1 tablespoon butter (optional)

8 tablespoons sugar-free maple-flavored syrup

*This recipe was tested with sucralose-based sugar substitute.

**Or, substitute 1/4 teaspoon ground cinnamon, 1/8 teaspoon ground ginger and pinch each ground allspice and ground nutmeg for 1/2 teaspoon pumpkin pie spice.

1. Combine flour, sugar substitute, baking powder, pumpkin pie spice, baking soda and salt in medium bowl.

2. Whisk together buttermilk, pumpkin, egg, oil and vanilla in small bowl. Add buttermilk mixture to flour mixture; stir until moist batter forms.

3. Spray griddle or large nonstick skillet with cooking spray; heat over medium-high heat. Spoon 2 tablespoons batter onto hot griddle for each pancake; spread to 3-inch diameter. Cook 2 to 3 minutes or until bubbles form on top. Turn and cook about 1 minute more or until bottoms are lightly browned. Serve with butter, if desired, and syrup. *Makes 8 servings*

Nutrients per Serving: 2 pancakes with 1 tablespoon syrup

Calories 107	**Fiber** 1g
Fat 3g (sat <1g)	**Cholesterol** 27mg
Protein 3g	**Sodium** 221mg
Carbohydrate 18g	

Exchanges: 1 starch, 1/2 fat

Cranberry Orange Ring

Apple Pancake Sandwich

Apple Pancake Sandwich

Quick Recipe   (Pictured above)

2 small Granny Smith apples
1/3 cup cholesterol-free egg substitute
2 tablespoons bacon bits
1/2 teaspoon sugar substitute*
1/4 teaspoon ground cinnamon
4 frozen pancakes
4 teaspoons sugar-free maple-flavored syrup

*This recipe was tested with sucralose-based sugar substitute.

Microwave Directions

1. Peel, core and chop apples (yields about 1 cup). Mix apples, egg substitute, bacon bits, sugar substitute and cinnamon in small bowl.

2. Place 2 frozen pancakes on small microwavable dish; top each with apple mixture. Microwave on HIGH 3 minutes.

3. Drizzle 2 teaspoons maple syrup over apple mixture on each pancake. Top each pancake with remaining pancakes to make sandwiches. Microwave on HIGH 2 minutes. Serve warm.

Makes 2 servings

Note: This recipe was tested in an 1100-watt microwave.

Nutrients per Serving: 1 sandwich

Calories 233	**Fiber** 3g
Fat 4g (sat 1g)	**Cholesterol** <11mg
Protein 11g	**Sodium** 655mg
Carbohydrate 37g	

Exchanges: 1-1/2 starch, 1 fruit, 1/2 lean meat, 1 fat

Fresh Plum Coffee Cake

2-1/4 cups all-purpose flour, divided
1/4 cup packed brown sugar
1/2 teaspoon ground cinnamon
1 tablespoon butter, softened
1-1/2 teaspoons baking powder
1/2 teaspoon baking soda
1/4 teaspoon salt
1 cup (8 ounces) lemon low-fat yogurt
2/3 cup granulated sugar
2 egg whites
1 egg
1 teaspoon grated lemon peel
4 medium plums, pitted and cut into
1/4-inch-thick slices

1. Preheat oven to 350°F. Spray 9-inch square baking pan with nonstick cooking spray.

2. For topping, combine 1/4 cup flour, brown sugar, cinnamon and butter in small bowl until crumbly; set aside.

3. Combine remaining 2 cups flour, baking powder, baking soda and salt in large bowl. Beat yogurt, granulated sugar, egg whites, egg and lemon peel in medium bowl with electric mixer at medium speed until well blended. Stir flour mixture into yogurt mixture just until ingredients are combined.

4. Pour batter into prepared pan. Arrange plums over batter; sprinkle evenly with reserved topping. Bake 30 to 35 minutes or until toothpick inserted into center of cake comes out clean. Cool in pan on wire rack. Serve warm or at room temperature.   *Makes 9 servings*

Nutrients per Serving: 1 coffee cake piece (1/9 of total recipe)

Calories 148	**Fiber** 1g
Fat 2g (sat <1g)	**Cholesterol** 14mg
Protein 3g	**Sodium** 134mg
Carbohydrate 30g	

Exchanges: 2 starch

Fruited Granola

(Pictured on page 48)

3 cups uncooked quick oats
1 cup sliced unblanched almonds
1 cup honey
1/2 cup toasted wheat germ
3 tablespoons butter, melted
1 teaspoon ground cinnamon
3 cups whole grain cereal flakes
1/2 cup dried blueberries or golden raisins
1/2 cup dried cranberries or cherries
1/2 cup dried banana chips or chopped pitted dates

1. Preheat oven to 325°F. Spread oats and almonds in 13×9-inch baking pan. Bake 15 minutes or until lightly toasted, stirring frequently.

2. Combine honey, wheat germ, butter and cinnamon in large bowl until well blended. Add oats and almonds; toss to coat completely. Spread mixture in single layer in same baking pan. Bake 20 minutes or until golden brown. Cool completely in pan on wire rack. Break mixture into chunks.

3. Combine oat chunks, cereal, blueberries, cranberries and banana chips in large bowl. Store in airtight container at room temperature up to 2 weeks.   *Makes 20 servings*

Nutrients per Serving: 1/2 cup granola

Calories 210	**Fiber** 4g
Fat 7g (sat 2g)	**Cholesterol** 5mg
Protein 5g	**Sodium** 58mg
Carbohydrate 36g	

Exchanges: 2 starch, 1-1/2 fat

Tip

Prepare this granola on the weekend, and you'll have a scrumptious snack or breakfast treat on hand for the rest of the week!

Blueberry Poppy Seed Coffee Cake

Blueberry Poppy Seed Coffee Cake

(Pictured at top left)

1-1/2 cups all-purpose flour
1/2 cup sugar
1 teaspoon baking powder
1/2 teaspoon baking soda
1/4 teaspoon salt
1/4 cup (1/2 stick) cold butter, cut into small pieces
1 tablespoon poppy seeds
3/4 cup low-fat buttermilk
1 egg
1 teaspoon vanilla extract
1 teaspoon grated lemon peel
1 cup fresh blueberries

1. Preheat oven to 350°F. Spray 9-inch round cake pan with nonstick cooking spray.

2. Combine flour, sugar, baking powder, baking soda and salt in large bowl. Cut in butter using pastry blender or two knives until mixture resembles coarse crumbs. Stir in poppy seeds.

3. Whisk buttermilk, egg, vanilla and lemon peel in small bowl until blended. Stir buttermilk mixture into flour mixture just until flour mixture is moistened. Spread half of batter into prepared pan; top with blueberries. Drop remaining batter in 8 dollops onto blueberries, leaving some berries uncovered. Bake 33 to 36 minutes or until top is golden brown.

4. Cool 15 minutes in pan on wire rack. Serve warm.   *Makes 8 servings*

Nutrients per Serving: 1 coffee cake wedge (1/8 of total recipe)

Calories 219	**Fiber** 1g
Fat 7g (sat 2g)	**Cholesterol** 27mg
Protein 4g	**Sodium** 313mg
Carbohydrate 34g	

Exchanges: 2 starch, 1-1/2 fat

Raisin Nut Bagels

Quick Recipe

2 ounces reduced-fat cream cheese
1-1/2 tablespoons chopped golden raisins
1-1/2 tablespoons chopped walnuts
1 teaspoon orange juice
1 sesame seed bagel, halved and toasted

Combine cream cheese, raisins, walnuts and orange juice in small bowl. Mix well. Spread cream cheese mixture on bagel halves.
Makes 2 servings

Nutrients per Serving: 1 bagel half with about 3 tablespoons spread

Calories 118	**Fiber** 1g
Fat 2g (sat <1g)	**Cholesterol** 10mg
Protein 8g	**Sodium** 408mg
Carbohydrate 18g	

Exchanges: 1-1/2 starch, 1/2 fruit, 1/2 fat

Good Morning Bread

(Pictured at bottom right)

- 1/4 cup water (70° to 80°F)
- 1 cup mashed ripe bananas (about 2 medium)
- 3 tablespoons canola oil
- 1 teaspoon salt
- 2-1/4 cups bread flour
- 3/4 cup whole wheat flour
- 3/4 cup chopped pitted dates
- 1/2 cup uncooked old-fashioned oats
- 1/4 cup nonfat dry milk powder
- 1 teaspoon grated orange peel (optional)
- 1 teaspoon ground cinnamon
- 2 teaspoons active dry yeast

Bread Machine Directions

1. Measuring carefully, place all ingredients in bread machine pan in order specified by owner's manual.

2. Program basic cycle and desired crust setting; press start. Immediately remove baked bread from pan; cool on wire rack. Serve with desired toppings. *Makes 20 servings*

Note: This recipe produces a moist, slightly dense loaf that has a lower volume than other loaves. The banana flavor is more prominent when the bread is toasted.

Nutrients per Serving: 1 slice bread (1/20 of loaf) without toppings

Calories 137	**Fiber** 2g
Fat 3g (sat <1g)	**Cholesterol** <1mg
Protein 4g	**Sodium** 124mg
Carbohydrate 26g	

Exchanges: 1 starch, 1/2 fruit, 1/2 fat

Chocolate-Covered Banana Slushy

- 3 cups fat-free (skim) milk, divided
- 1/4 cup no-sugar-added chocolate instant beverage mix
- 1 medium banana

1. Combine 2 cups milk and beverage mix in a pitcher; whisk until powder dissolves.

2. Pour chocolate milk into ice cube trays (about 2 tablespoons per cube). Freeze until solid (about 2 hours).

3. Remove cubes from trays. Place in blender container. Pour remaining 1 cup milk over cubes. Cover; blend until slushy, stopping to scrape blender sides as necessary.

4. Add banana. Blend until slushy. Serve immediately. *Makes 4 servings*

Nutrients per Serving: 1 cup slushy

Calories 118	**Fiber** 1g
Fat 1g (sat <1g)	**Cholesterol** 4mg
Protein 6g	**Sodium** 132mg
Carbohydrate 22g	

Exchanges: 1/2 fruit, 1 milk

Good Morning Bread

Pineapple Crunch Coffee Cake

(Pictured at right)

- **1-3/4 cups reduced-fat baking mix**
- **1/2 cup plus 2 tablespoons fat-free (skim) milk**
- **1/2 cup toasted wheat germ**
- **1/2 cup reduced-fat sour cream**
- **1/4 cup granulated sugar**
- **1 egg, beaten**
- **1 teaspoon vanilla extract**
- **2 cans (8 ounces each) crushed pineapple in unsweetened juice, drained**
- **1/3 cup packed dark brown sugar**
- **1/3 cup uncooked old-fashioned oats**

1. Preheat oven to 350°F. Coat 8-inch square baking dish with nonstick cooking spray.

2. Combine baking mix, milk, wheat germ, sour cream, granulated sugar, egg and vanilla in medium bowl. Stir until dry ingredients are moistened. (Batter will be lumpy.) Spread batter in prepared baking dish. Spoon pineapple evenly over batter. Sprinkle brown sugar and oats over pineapple.

3. Bake 30 minutes or until toothpick inserted into center comes out clean. Serve warm or at room temperature. *Makes 9 servings*

Nutrients per Serving: 1 coffee cake square (1/9 of total recipe)

Calories 237	**Fiber** 2g
Fat 4g (sat 1g)	**Cholesterol** 28mg
Protein 6g	**Sodium** 267mg
Carbohydrate 44g	

Exchanges: 2-1/2 starch, 1/2 fruit, 1/2 fat

Tip

When making quick-batter breads, such as this coffee cake, stir just until dry ingredients are moistened; the batter should look lumpy when it goes into the baking dish. Too much stirring will give the cake a tough texture with lots of holes.

Home-Style Hash Brown Pancakes

meatless · cooking for 1 or 2

Quick Recipe

- **2 large egg whites**
- **1 teaspoon skim milk**
- **1 large potato with skin**
- **1/2 cup grated CABOT® 50% Light Cheddar (2 ounces)**
- **1 tablespoon all-purpose flour**
- **1/8 teaspoon salt**
- **1 tablespoon canola oil**
- **1/4 cup CABOT® No Fat Sour Cream**
- **1 green onion, green part only, minced**

1. In medium bowl, whisk together egg whites and milk.

2. Grate potato into egg mixture. Stir in cheese, flour and salt.

3. In large nonstick pan over medium heat, heat oil. Drop potato mixture into pan to form two "pancakes." Cook until golden brown, about 5 minutes per side.

4. In small bowl, mix together sour cream and green onion; spoon on top of pancakes. *Makes 2 servings*

Nutrients per Serving: 1 pancake with about 2 tablespoons sour cream mixture

Calories 283	**Fiber** 3g
Fat 11g (sat 4g)	**Cholesterol** 15mg
Protein 15g	**Sodium** 420mg
Carbohydrate 31g	

Exchanges: 2 starch, 1-1/2 lean meat, 1 fat

Pineapple Crunch Coffee Cake

Potato-Zucchini Pancakes with Warm Corn Salsa

Potato-Zucchini Pancakes with Warm Corn Salsa

low fat   meatless

Quick Recipe   (Pictured above)

Warm Corn Salsa (recipe follows)
2 cups refrigerated or frozen hash brown potatoes, thawed
1-1/2 cups shredded zucchini, drained
1/2 cup cholesterol-free egg substitute
1/4 cup all-purpose flour
2 tablespoons chopped onion
2 tablespoons chopped green bell pepper
1/4 teaspoon salt
1/8 teaspoon black pepper
Nonstick cooking spray

1. Prepare Warm Corn Salsa; keep warm.

2. Combine potatoes, zucchini, egg substitute, flour, onion, bell pepper, salt and black pepper in medium bowl until well blended.

3. Spray large nonstick skillet with cooking spray; heat over medium-high heat until hot. Drop potato mixture by 1/4 cupfuls into skillet. Cook pancakes about 3 minutes on each side or

until golden brown. Place 2 pancakes on serving plate; top with 1/2 cup Warm Corn Salsa.   *Makes 6 servings*

Warm Corn Salsa

Nonstick cooking spray
2 tablespoons chopped onion
2 tablespoons finely chopped green bell pepper
1 package (10 ounces) frozen corn, thawed
1 cup chunky salsa
2 teaspoons chopped fresh cilantro

1. Spray small nonstick skillet with cooking spray; heat over medium heat until hot. Add onion and bell pepper; cook and stir 3 minutes or until crisp-tender.

2. Add corn, salsa and cilantro. Reduce heat to medium-low. Cook 5 minutes or until hot.   *Makes 3 cups*

Nutrients per Serving: 2 pancakes with 1/2 cup salsa

Calories 110	**Fiber** 3g
Fat <1g (sat <1g)	**Cholesterol** 0mg
Protein 5g	**Sodium** 437mg
Carbohydrate 24g	

Exchanges: 1 starch, 2 vegetable

Tip

Small zucchini are tender and flavorful, while larger ones have a lower water content and a slightly mealy texture. Zucchini does not need to be peeled, since it has a very thin, edible skin. If you purchase your zucchini ahead of time, refrigerate it, unwashed, in a perforated plastic bag for up to 5 days.

Sausage and Cheddar Omelet

Quick Recipe   (Pictured at bottom right)

2 uncooked turkey sausage breakfast links (about 1 ounce each)

1 small onion, diced

Nonstick cooking spray

1-1/2 cups cholesterol-free egg substitute

1/4 teaspoon black pepper

1/2 cup (2 ounces) shredded reduced-fat cheddar cheese, divided

2 to 3 tablespoons sliced green onions (optional)

1. Heat 12-inch nonstick skillet over medium-high heat. Remove sausage casings. Add sausage and diced onion to skillet. Cook about 5 minutes or until sausage is no longer pink and onion is crisp-tender, stirring to separate meat. Remove from skillet; set aside.

2. Wipe out skillet with paper towel; spray with cooking spray. Heat over medium heat. Pour egg substitute into skillet; sprinkle with pepper. Cook about 2 minutes or until bottom is set, lifting edge of omelet with spatula to allow uncooked portion to flow underneath. Reduce heat to medium-low. Cover; cook 4 minutes or until top of omelet is set.

3. Gently slide cooked omelet onto large serving plate; spoon reserved sausage mixture down center of egg. Sprinkle with 1/4 cup cheese. Carefully fold 2 opposite sides of omelet over sausage mixture to cover. Sprinkle with remaining 1/4 cup cheese and sliced green onions, if desired. Cut in half; serve immediately. *Makes 2 servings*

Nutrients per Serving: 1/2 omelet

Calories 266	**Fiber** 1g
Fat 12g (sat 6g)	**Cholesterol** 38mg
Protein 30g	**Sodium** 751mg
Carbohydrate 8g	

Exchanges: 2 vegetable, 4 lean meat

Banana Yogurt Shake

Quick Recipe

1-1/2 cups 2% low-fat milk

2 ripe bananas, peeled

1 cup low-fat plain yogurt

1/4 cup honey

1 teaspoon vanilla

1/2 teaspoon ground cinnamon

Dash ground nutmeg

5 ice cubes

Combine all ingredients except ice cubes in blender or food processor; process until thick and creamy. With motor running, add ice cubes; process until smooth. Pour into tall glasses to serve. *Makes 4 cups*

Favorite recipe from **National Honey Board**

Nutrients per Serving: 1 cup shake

Calories 206	**Fiber** 2g
Fat 3g (sat 2g)	**Cholesterol** 11mg
Protein 7g	**Sodium** 90mg
Carbohydrate 40g	

Exchanges: 1 fruit, 1 starch, 1 milk, 1/2 fat

Sausage and Cheddar Omelet

Potato Latke Sandwich

Quick Recipe   *(Pictured at right)*

> **Nonstick cooking spray**
> **4 cups refrigerated or frozen shredded potatoes, thawed**
> **3/4 cup cholesterol-free egg substitute**
> **1 teaspoon black pepper**
> **2 ounces fat-free cream cheese**
> **1/4 cup chopped green onions**
> **3 tablespoons bacon bits**
> **4 tablespoons unsweetened applesauce**

1. Preheat oven to 425°F. Spray baking sheet with cooking spray.

2. Combine potatoes, egg substitute and pepper in medium bowl. Shape mixture into 8 patties (1/2 cup each); place on baking sheet. Bake 15 minutes. Remove from oven. Spray patties with cooking spray; turn patties over. Bake 6 minutes or until golden brown. Cool 5 minutes.

3. Blend cream cheese, onions and bacon bits in small bowl until creamy.

4. Spread 4 potato patties with 2 tablespoons cream cheese spread and 1 tablespoon applesauce; top with remaining potato patties.
Makes 4 servings

Nutrients per Serving: 1 sandwich

Calories 247	**Fiber** 4g
Fat 3g (sat <1g)	**Cholesterol** 6mg
Protein 14g	**Sodium** 370mg
Carbohydrate 42g	

Exchanges: 3 starch, 1 lean meat

Ham and Vegetable Omelet

Quick Recipe   *(Pictured on page 48)*

> **Nonstick cooking spray**
> **2 ounces (about 1/2 cup) diced 95% fat-free turkey ham**
> **1 small onion, diced**
> **1/2 medium green bell pepper, diced**
> **1/2 medium red bell pepper, diced**
> **2 cloves garlic, minced**
> **1-1/2 cups cholesterol-free egg substitute**
> **1/8 teaspoon black pepper**
> **1/2 cup (2 ounces) shredded reduced-fat Colby cheese, divided**
> **1 medium tomato, chopped**

1. Spray 12-inch nonstick skillet with cooking spray; heat over medium-high heat until hot. Add ham, onion, bell peppers and garlic; cook and stir 5 minutes or until vegetables are crisp-tender. Transfer mixture to large bowl; set aside.

2. Wipe out skillet with paper towel; spray with cooking spray. Heat over medium-high heat. Pour egg substitute into skillet; sprinkle with black pepper. Cook over medium-high heat about 2 minutes or until bottom is set, lifting edge of omelet with spatula to allow uncooked portion to flow underneath. Reduce heat to medium-low. Cover; cook 4 minutes or until top of omelet is set.

3. Gently slide cooked omelet onto large serving plate; spoon reserved ham mixture down center of egg. Sprinkle with 1/4 cup cheese. Carefully fold 2 opposite sides of omelet over ham mixture to cover. Sprinkle with remaining 1/4 cup cheese and tomato. Cut in half; serve immediately.   *Makes 2 servings*

Nutrients per Serving: 1/2 omelet

Calories 252	**Fiber** 2g
Fat 8g (sat 4g)	**Cholesterol** 34mg
Protein 32g	**Sodium** 886mg
Carbohydrate 16g	

Exchanges: 3 vegetable, 4 lean meat

Potato Latke Sandwich

Cranberry Cheese Crêpe

Cranberry Cheese Crêpes

(Pictured above)

Festive Cranberry Sauce (recipe follows)
1 cup all-purpose flour
3 tablespoons sugar, divided
1/4 teaspoon salt
1 cup fat-free (skim) milk
2 egg whites
1 egg
1 tablespoon butter, melted
Nonstick cooking spray
3/4 cup low-fat (1%) cottage cheese
4 ounces fat-free cream cheese, softened
1 teaspoon vanilla extract
3 tablespoons toasted sliced almonds*

To toast nuts, spread in shallow baking pan. Bake in preheated 350°F oven 5 to 10 minutes or until fragrant, stirring occasionally.

1. Prepare Festive Cranberry Sauce; set aside. Combine flour, 1 tablespoon sugar and salt in medium bowl; whisk in milk, egg whites, egg and butter until smooth. Batter can be covered and refrigerated up to 1 hour.

2. Spray 8-inch nonstick skillet with cooking spray. Heat over medium heat until hot. Remove from heat. Pour in scant 1/4 cup batter; tilt skillet to coat surface. When edges of batter curl away from side of skillet, flip crêpe; brown other side. Repeat with remaining batter.

3. Place cottage cheese in food processor or blender; process until smooth. Add cream cheese, remaining 2 tablespoons sugar and vanilla; process until smooth.

4. Preheat oven to 350°F. Spread 2 tablespoons cheese mixture down center of each crêpe. Spread 2 tablespoons Festive Cranberry Sauce over cheese mixture. Fold up sides of crêpes; place in 15×10×1-inch jelly-roll pan. Bake 5 minutes or until heated through.

5. Place crêpes on serving plates. Top each crêpe with 1 tablespoon sauce and 1 teaspoon almonds. *Makes 8 servings*

Festive Cranberry Sauce

1 package (12 ounces) fresh or frozen cranberries, thawed
2/3 cup sugar
1 cup water, divided
1/2 teaspoon almond extract (optional)
2 tablespoons cornstarch

1. Combine cranberries, sugar and 3/4 cup water in medium saucepan. Bring to a boil over medium-high heat; reduce heat to low. Simmer, uncovered, 5 minutes or until cranberries are tender and sugar is dissolved. Stir in almond extract, if desired.

2. Return mixture to a boil over medium-high heat. Stir remaining 1/4 cup water into cornstarch in small bowl until smooth; stir into cranberry mixture. Boil 1 minute or until thickened, stirring constantly. Remove from heat. *Makes about 2-1/2 cups*

Nutrients per Serving: 1 serving

Calories 263	**Fiber** 2g
Fat 4g (sat 1g)	**Cholesterol** 31mg
Protein 10g	**Sodium** 293mg
Carbohydrate 47g	

Exchanges: 2 starch, 1 fruit, 1/2 lean meat, 1/2 fat

Cornmeal-Pecan Pancakes

Quick Recipe (Pictured at bottom right)

> 1 cup yellow cornmeal
> 1/4 cup all-purpose flour
> 1/3 cup sugar substitute*
> 1 teaspoon baking powder
> 1/2 teaspoon baking soda
> 1/4 teaspoon salt
> 1/8 teaspoon nutmeg
> 1 cup low-fat buttermilk
> 1 egg
> 1 tablespoon canola oil
> 1/2 teaspoon vanilla
> 1/4 cup chopped pecans
> Nonstick cooking spray
> 8 tablespoons sugar-free maple-flavored syrup

This recipe was tested with sucralose-based sugar substitute.

1. Combine cornmeal, flour, sugar substitute, baking powder, baking soda, salt and nutmeg in large bowl. Combine buttermilk, egg, oil and vanilla in medium bowl. Add buttermilk mixture to cornmeal mixture; stir until smooth. Stir in pecans.

2. Spray griddle or large nonstick skillet with cooking spray; heat over medium-high heat. Spoon 2 tablespoons batter onto hot griddle for each pancake; spread to 3-inch diameter. Cook 2 to 3 minutes or until bubbles form on top. Turn and cook 1 minute more or until bottoms are lightly browned. Serve with syrup.

Makes 8 servings

Nutrients per Serving: 2 pancakes with 1 tablespoon syrup

Calories 150	**Fiber** 1g
Fat 6g (sat 1g)	**Cholesterol** 28mg
Protein 4g	**Sodium** 268mg
Carbohydrate 23g	

Exchanges: 1-1/2 starch, 1 fat

Mini Waffles with Sweet Strawberries

Quick Recipe

> 1-1/2 teaspoons sugar substitute*
> 2 tablespoons orange juice
> 1/2 teaspoon grated orange peel (optional)
> 1 cup sliced strawberries
> 16 frozen mini waffles *or* 4 regular waffles
> 1/4 cup reduced-fat sour cream

This recipe was tested with sucralose-based sugar substitute.

1. Combine sugar substitute, orange juice and orange peel, if desired, in medium bowl. Add strawberries; toss to coat. Let stand 20 minutes.

2. Toast waffles. Place 4 mini waffles on each of 4 plates. Top each serving with 1 tablespoon sour cream and 1/4 cup berry mixture.

Makes 4 servings

Nutrients per Serving: 1 serving

Calories 299	**Fiber** 3g
Fat 10g (sat 3g)	**Cholesterol** 30mg
Protein 8g	**Sodium** 610mg
Carbohydrate 45g	

Exchanges: 2-1/2 starch, 1/2 fruit, 1-1/2 fat

Cornmeal-Pecan Pancakes

Main Dishes

ઝ ઝ ઝ

Chicken Veggie Pasta

Quick Recipe   *(Pictured at left)*

8 ounces medium shell pasta
3 cups diced cooked chicken breasts
1 medium red bell pepper, cut into 1-1/2×1/4-inch strips
1 package (6 ounces) frozen snow peas, thawed and drained
1/4 cup sliced green onions
3/4 cup reduced-fat oil and vinegar dressing
1 cup cherry tomatoes, halved
Lettuce leaves (optional)

1. Cook pasta according to package directions, omitting salt; drain and cool.

2. Combine chicken, pasta, red pepper, snow peas and green onions in large bowl. Pour dressing over top; toss to mix. Cover and chill until ready to serve. Add tomatoes; toss gently. Serve on lettuce-lined plates, if desired.   *Makes 6 servings*

Nutrients per Serving: 2/3 cup pasta mixture

Calories 310	**Fiber** 3g
Fat 3g (sat 1g)	**Cholesterol** 54mg
Protein 27g	**Sodium** 511mg
Carbohydrate 42g	

Exchanges: 2 starch, 2 vegetable, 2 lean meat

Clockwise from top left: Chicken Veggie Pasta, Vegetable Fajitas with Spicy Salsa (page 83), Grilled Fish with Buttery Lemon Parsley (page 66) and Orange-Ginger Tofu & Noodles (page 68)

65

Meat Crust Pie

(Pictured at right)

1 pound 95% lean ground beef

2 cans (8 ounces each) tomato sauce, divided

1/2 cup seasoned dry bread crumbs

1/2 cup chopped green bell pepper, divided

1/4 cup minced onion

3/4 teaspoon salt, divided

1/8 teaspoon dried oregano

1/8 teaspoon black pepper

1 cup water

1-1/3 cups uncooked instant rice

1 cup (4 ounces) shredded reduced-fat cheddar cheese, divided

1. Preheat oven to 350°F. Combine beef, 1/2 cup tomato sauce, bread crumbs, 1/4 cup bell pepper, onion, 1/4 teaspoon salt, oregano and black pepper in large bowl; mix well. Pat mixture onto bottom and up side of ungreased 9-inch deep-dish pie plate.

2. Bring water and remaining 1/2 teaspoon salt to a boil in medium saucepan; stir in rice. Cover; remove from heat. Let stand 5 minutes or until water is absorbed. Add remaining 1-1/2 cups tomato sauce, 1/2 cup cheese and remaining 1/4 cup bell pepper to rice; mix well. Spoon rice mixture into meat shell. Cover with foil; bake 25 minutes.

3. Remove from oven; drain fat carefully, holding pan lid over top to keep pie from sliding. Top with remaining 1/2 cup cheese. Bake, uncovered, 10 to 15 minutes or until meat juices run clear and cheese is melted. Carefully drain fat again. Cut into wedges to serve.

Makes 8 servings

Nutrients per Serving: 1 pie wedge (1/8 of total recipe)

Calories 290	**Fiber** 1g
Fat 6g (sat 3g)	**Cholesterol** 37mg
Protein 19g	**Sodium** 778mg
Carbohydrate 39g	

Exchanges: 2 starch, 1 vegetable, 2 lean meat

Grilled Fish with Buttery Lemon Parsley

low carb

Quick Recipe   (Pictured on page 64)

Nonstick cooking spray

6 tablespoons yogurt-based diet margarine

3 tablespoons finely chopped fresh parsley

1 teaspoon grated lemon peel

1/2 teaspoon salt

1/2 teaspoon dried rosemary

6 lean white fish fillets (6 ounces each), such as grouper, snapper or any lean white fish

3 medium lemons, halved

1. Spray cold grid of grill with cooking spray. Preheat grill to medium-high heat.

2. Combine margarine, parsley, lemon peel, salt and rosemary in small bowl; set aside.

3. Coat fish with cooking spray; place on grid. Grill, uncovered, 3 minutes. Turn fish over; grill 2 to 3 minutes longer or until fish flakes when tested with fork.

4. To serve, squeeze juice from 1 lemon half evenly over each fillet. Top with equal amounts of parsley mixture.   *Makes 6 servings*

Nutrients per Serving: 1 fish fillet with about 1 tablespoon parsley mixture

Calories 211	**Fiber** <1g
Fat 7g (sat 1g)	**Cholesterol** 63mg
Protein 33g	**Sodium** 423mg
Carbohydrate 2g	

Exchanges: 5 lean meat

Tip

Because fish cooks quickly, watch it closely while grilling. The fish is done when it feels slightly springy, looks opaque and has lost all its translucency.

Meat Crust Pie

Family-Style Beef Pizza

(Pictured at right)

1 package (about 13.8 ounces) refrigerated pizza dough
1/4 pound 95% lean ground beef
3 tablespoons finely chopped onion
3/4 cup pizza sauce
1 small tomato, peeled, seeded and chopped
2 teaspoons Italian seasoning
2 cloves garlic, minced
1/8 teaspoon ground red pepper
1/2 cup sliced mushrooms
1 cup (4 ounces) shredded part-skim mozzarella cheese
1 tablespoon finely grated Parmesan cheese

1. Preheat oven to 425°F. Lightly spray 12-inch pizza pan with nonstick cooking spray. Unroll pizza dough; press onto prepared pan. Build up edges slightly. Prick dough all over with fork. Bake 7 to 10 minutes or until lightly browned.

2. Meanwhile, brown ground beef and onion in large skillet over medium-high heat, stirring to separate meat. Drain fat.

3. Bring pizza sauce, tomato, Italian seasoning, garlic and red pepper to a boil in small saucepan over medium heat, stirring frequently. Reduce heat; simmer, uncovered, about 8 minutes or until desired consistency.

4. Spread tomato sauce evenly over pizza crust. Sprinkle with ground beef mixture and mushrooms. Sprinkle with cheeses. Bake 5 to 8 minutes or until heated through.

Makes 6 servings

Nutrients per Serving: 1 pizza wedge (1/6 of total recipe)

Calories 259	**Fiber** 2g
Fat 6g (sat 2g)	**Cholesterol** 23mg
Protein 15g	**Sodium** 723mg
Carbohydrate 35g	

Exchanges: 2 starch, 1/2 vegetable, 1-1/2 lean meat

Orange-Ginger Tofu & Noodles

(Pictured on page 64)

2/3 cup orange juice
3 tablespoons reduced-sodium soy sauce
1 clove garlic, minced
1/2 to 1 teaspoon minced fresh ginger
1/4 teaspoon red pepper flakes
5 ounces extra-firm tofu, well drained* and cut into 1/2-inch cubes
1-1/2 teaspoons cornstarch
1 teaspoon canola oil
2 cups fresh cut-up vegetables, such as broccoli, carrots, onion and snow peas
1-1/2 cups hot cooked vermicelli

*Tofu must be drained before stir-frying. Remove any remaining water by placing the block of tofu on several layers of paper towels. Cover it with additional paper towels weighted down with a heavy plate. Let it stand 15 to 20 minutes before cutting into cubes.

1. Combine orange juice, soy sauce, garlic, ginger and red pepper flakes in resealable food storage bag; add tofu. Marinate 20 to 30 minutes. Drain tofu, reserving marinade. Stir marinade into cornstarch in small bowl until smooth.

2. Heat oil in large nonstick skillet or wok over medium-high heat. Add vegetables; stir-fry 2 to 3 minutes or until vegetables are crisp-tender. Add tofu; stir-fry 1 minute. Stir reserved marinade mixture; add to skillet. Bring to a boil; boil 1 minute. Serve over noodles.

Makes 2 servings

Nutrients per Serving: 2 cups tofu mixture with 3/4 cup cooked vermicelli

Calories 305	**Fiber** 6g
Fat 7g (sat 1g)	**Cholesterol** 0mg
Protein 19g	**Sodium** 824mg
Carbohydrate 42g	

Exchanges: 2 starch, 2 vegetable, 1 lean meat, 1 fat

Family-Style Beef Pizza

Beef & Veggie Lasagna

high fiber

    6 whole wheat lasagna noodles
      Nonstick cooking spray
  3/4 pound 95% lean ground beef
    2 cups finely chopped red bell peppers
1-1/2 cups pasta sauce with onion and garlic
    1 package (10 ounces) frozen spinach,
      thawed and squeezed dry
    1 tablespoon dried basil
  1/4 teaspoon *each* salt and black pepper
    1 cup fat-free ricotta cheese
    1 cup (4 ounces) shredded part-skim
      mozzarella cheese
    2 tablespoons grated Parmesan cheese
      (optional)

1. Preheat oven to 350°F. Cook pasta according to package directions, omitting salt; drain.

2. Meanwhile, spray 12-inch nonstick skillet with cooking spray. Brown beef over medium-high heat, stirring to separate meat. Drain fat. Add bell peppers, pasta sauce, spinach, basil, salt and pepper. Bring to a boil. Reduce heat; simmer, covered, 10 minutes or until peppers are tender. Set aside.

3. Spray 11×7-inch baking dish with cooking spray. Place two lasagna noodles in dish. Spread 1-1/2 cups sauce mixture over noodles. Spoon 1/2 cup ricotta cheese evenly over sauce. Repeat layers once.

4. Top with remaining noodles and 1-1/2 cups sauce, making sure sauce covers noodles completely. Cover with foil. Bake 25 minutes. Sprinkle mozzarella cheese evenly over lasagna. Bake, uncovered, 5 minutes or until cheese melts. Sprinkle with Parmesan cheese, if desired. Let lasagna stand 10 minutes.

Makes 6 servings

Nutrients per Serving: 1 (3-1/2-inch) square

Calories 301	**Fiber** 5g
Fat 7g (sat 3g)	**Cholesterol** 48mg
Protein 26g	**Sodium** 517mg
Carbohydrate 32g	

Exchanges: 1-1/2 starch, 2 vegetable, 2-1/2 lean meat

Cinnamon Pork with Sweet Potatoes

high fiber

Quick Recipe

    2 medium sweet potatoes (about
      14 ounces total)
    2 tablespoons water
  1/2 cup pineapple juice or apricot nectar
    2 teaspoons cornstarch
  1/4 teaspoon salt
    2 medium tart apples, such as McIntosh
1-1/4 pounds pork tenderloin, halved
      lengthwise and cut into 1/4-inch
      slices
    1 teaspoon ground cinnamon
  1/4 teaspoon black pepper
      Nonstick cooking spray
    1 tablespoon olive oil

1. Peel sweet potatoes. Cut potatoes lengthwise into quarters. Cut each quarter into 1/4-inch-thick slices. Place sweet potatoes and water in microwavable dish. Microwave, covered, on HIGH 4 to 5 minutes or until potatoes are just tender. Drain; set aside.

2. Combine pineapple juice, cornstarch and salt in small bowl until smooth; set aside. Core apples; cut each apple into 16 wedges. Toss pork with cinnamon and pepper in large bowl; set aside.

3. Spray large nonstick skillet or wok with cooking spray. Heat skillet over medium heat. Add apples; cook 2 minutes or until tender, stirring frequently. Remove from skillet.

4. Add oil to skillet; cook and stir pork in batches over medium-high heat 2 to 3 minutes or until no longer pink.

5. Return pork and apples to skillet. Stir pineapple juice mixture; stir into skillet. Bring to a boil. Reduce heat; simmer, uncovered, 1 minute or until thickened. Gently stir in sweet potatoes.

Makes 4 servings

Nutrients per Serving: 2 cups

Calories 348	**Fiber** 6g
Fat 7g (sat 2g)	**Cholesterol** 91mg
Protein 32g	**Sodium** 262mg
Carbohydrate 37g	

Exchanges: 2-1/2 starch, 4 lean meat

Autumn Pasta

high fiber · **cooking for 1 or 2**

Quick Recipe   *(Pictured below)*

2 boneless skinless chicken breasts (about 1/4 pound each), cut into 1/2-inch cubes

8 brussels sprouts, trimmed and sliced

1 large bulb fennel, trimmed, quartered and sliced

2 medium tomatoes, chopped

1/4 cup lemon juice

1 tablespoon olive oil

1 teaspoon minced garlic

Nonstick cooking spray

1 cup cooked whole-grain rotini pasta

2 tablespoons grated Parmesan cheese

1. Combine chicken, brussels sprouts, fennel, tomatoes, lemon juice, olive oil and garlic in large bowl.

2. Lightly coat large skillet with cooking spray; heat over medium heat. Add chicken mixture; cook, covered, about 15 minutes or until vegetables are tender and chicken is cooked through.

3. Add pasta to skillet with chicken mixture and heat through. Sprinkle with cheese before serving.   *Makes 2 servings*

Nutrients per Serving: 2-1/4 cups pasta mixture

Calories 372	**Fiber** 6g
Fat 12g (sat 3g)	**Cholesterol** 71mg
Protein 35g	**Sodium** 184mg
Carbohydrate 34g	

Exchanges: 1-1/2 starch, 2-1/2 vegetable, 3-1/2 lean meat

Autumn Pasta

Smothered Patties with Onion

Quick Recipe   (Pictured at right)

> 1 pound 95% lean ground beef
> 1/8 teaspoon salt
>   Nonstick cooking spray
> 1 medium onion, thinly sliced
> 3/4 cup water
> 2 teaspoons beef bouillon granules
> 1 teaspoon Worcestershire sauce
> 1/2 teaspoon decaffeinated or regular instant coffee granules
> 1/8 teaspoon black pepper

1. Shape ground beef into 4 (1/2-inch-thick) patties. Sprinkle with salt.

2. Lightly spray large skillet with cooking spray. Heat over medium-high heat. Add patties; cook 3 minutes on each side or until just barely pink in center. Remove from skillet; set aside.

3. Lightly spray small skillet with cooking spray. Add onion; cook, stirring frequently, 3 minutes or until tender. Remove from skillet; set aside.

4. Combine water, bouillon, Worcestershire sauce, coffee granules and pepper in large skillet. Bring to a boil; boil 3 minutes or until mixture is reduced to 1/2 cup.

5. Return patties and onion to skillet. Cook 1 minute or until heated through, turning patties several times to coat with sauce.

Makes 4 servings

Serving Suggestion: Serve with mashed potatoes and steamed green beans.

Nutrients per Serving: 1 patty with 1/4 cup onion mixture

Calories 169	**Fiber** 0g
Fat 5g (sat 2g)	**Cholesterol** 69mg
Protein 24g	**Sodium** 135mg
Carbohydrate 4g	

Exchanges: 1 vegetable, 3 lean meat

Feta and Spinach Stuffed Turkey Patties

Quick Recipe

> 1/4 cup cornflake crumbs
> 1/4 cup sliced green onions
> 3 tablespoons cholesterol-free egg substitute
> 1 pound 93% lean ground turkey
> 1/2 (10-ounce) package frozen chopped spinach, thawed and squeezed dry
> 1/3 cup crumbled reduced-fat feta cheese
> 1/4 cup chopped black olives
> 1/4 teaspoon black pepper
> 1/2 cup chopped fresh tomato

1. Spray cold grid of grill with nonstick cooking spray. Prepare grill for direct grilling.

2. Combine cornflake crumbs, green onions and egg substitute in medium bowl. Add ground turkey; mix well. Shape turkey mixture into 8 (3/8-inch-thick) patties on sheet of waxed paper.

3. Combine spinach, feta cheese, olives and pepper in small bowl; mix until blended. Place about 3 tablespoons spinach mixture on top of 4 turkey patties. Top with remaining patties, pressing edges to seal.

4. Grill patties over medium heat 11 to 13 minutes or until cooked through (165°F). Serve topped with chopped tomato.

Makes 4 servings

Nutrients per Serving: 1 patty with 2 tablespoons tomato

Calories 190	**Fiber** 2g
Fat 4g (sat 1g)	**Cholesterol** 48mg
Protein 31g	**Sodium** 403mg
Carbohydrate 8g	

Exchanges: 4 lean meat

Smothered Patty with Onion

Black Bean and Green Chile Tostadas

high fiber   meatless

Quick Recipe   *(Pictured at right)*

1 cup rinsed and drained canned black beans, mashed
1 can (4 ounces) chopped mild green chiles
2 teaspoons chili powder
  Nonstick cooking spray
4 (6-inch) corn tortillas
1 cup torn romaine lettuce leaves
1 cup chopped seeded fresh tomato
1/2 cup chopped green onions
1/2 cup (2 ounces) shredded reduced-fat cheddar cheese
1/4 cup fat-free sour cream
  Fresh cilantro sprigs (optional)

1. Combine beans, chiles and chili powder in small saucepan; cook, stirring occasionally, over medium heat 5 minutes or until heated through.

2. Spray large nonstick skillet with cooking spray; heat over medium heat. Lightly sprinkle tortillas with water; place in skillet, one at a time. Cook each tortilla 20 to 30 seconds or until hot and pliable, turning once.

3. Spread bean mixture evenly over tortillas; layer each tortilla with 1/4 cup lettuce, 1/4 cup tomato, 2 tablespoons onions, 2 tablespoons cheese and 1 tablespoon sour cream. Garnish with cilantro sprigs, if desired.

Makes 4 servings

Nutrients per Serving: 1 tostada

Calories 191	**Fiber** 8g
Fat 5g (sat 2g)	**Cholesterol** 11mg
Protein 10g	**Sodium** 464mg
Carbohydrate 28g	

Exchanges: 1-1/2 starch, 1 vegetable, 1 lean meat

Grilled Caramelized Salmon and Asparagus

1 salmon fillet with skin (1 pound, 1 inch thick)
2 tablespoons packed brown sugar
1 tablespoon grated orange peel
1 teaspoon minced garlic
1/2 teaspoon salt
1/8 to 1/4 teaspoon ground red pepper
  Nonstick cooking spray
16 asparagus spears, trimmed
1/4 teaspoon black pepper
1 cup finely chopped fresh pineapple

1. Place salmon, skin side down, in shallow dish. Combine brown sugar, orange peel, garlic, salt and red pepper in small bowl. Rub onto fish. Cover; refrigerate 2 to 8 hours.

2. Spray cold grill grid with cooking spray. Prepare grill for direct grilling.

3. Lightly coat asparagus with cooking spray. Sprinkle with black pepper.

4. Remove salmon from dish. Discard any liquid. Grill salmon, skin side down, on covered grill over medium heat 6 minutes. Place asparagus spears beside salmon on grill. Grill, covered, turning asparagus occasionally, about 4 minutes more or until salmon just begins to flake when tested with fork and asparagus begins to brown.

5. Cut salmon into 4 equal pieces. Top salmon with fresh pineapple and serve with asparagus.

Makes 4 servings

Nutrients per Serving: 3-1/2 ounces salmon (cooked weight) with 1/4 cup pineapple and 4 asparagus spears

Calories 277	**Fiber** 3g
Fat 12g (sat 3g)	**Cholesterol** 66mg
Protein 25g	**Sodium** 363mg
Carbohydrate 17g	

Exchanges: 1 fruit, 1 vegetable, 3 lean meat, 1/2 fat

Black Bean and Green Chile Tostada

Herbed Turkey Breast with Orange Sauce

Herbed Turkey Breast with Orange Sauce

low fat | low sodium | low carb

(Pictured above)

1 large onion, chopped
3 cloves garlic, minced
1 teaspoon dried rosemary
1/2 teaspoon black pepper
1 boneless skinless turkey breast
(2 to 3 pounds)
1-1/2 cups orange juice
Fresh rosemary sprigs (optional)

Slow Cooker Directions

1. Place onion in slow cooker. Combine garlic, rosemary and pepper in small bowl; set aside.

2. Cut slices about three-fourths of the way through turkey at 2-inch intervals. Rub garlic mixture between slices.

3. Place turkey, cut side up, in slow cooker. Pour orange juice over turkey.

4. Cover; cook on LOW 7 to 8 hours. Serve turkey with sauce and fresh rosemary, if desired.
Makes 6 servings

Nutrients per Serving: about 4 ounces turkey (cooked weight) with 1/3 cup sauce

Calories 203	**Fiber** 1g
Fat 1g (sat <1g)	**Cholesterol** 99mg
Protein 36g	**Sodium** 70mg
Carbohydrate 10g	

Exchanges: 1/2 fruit, 1/2 vegetable, 4 lean meat

Shrimp & Tomato Stir-Fry

low carb

Quick Recipe

20 kalamata olives, pitted and coarsely chopped
1 cup cherry tomatoes, halved
1/4 cup chopped fresh basil
1/4 teaspoon plus 1/8 teaspoon salt, divided
1/4 teaspoon black pepper
Nonstick cooking spray
1 pound peeled medium raw shrimp
1 clove garlic, minced
1/8 teaspoon red pepper flakes
1 medium zucchini, quartered lengthwise, then cut crosswise into 2-inch pieces
1 medium onion, cut into 8 wedges

1. Gently toss olives, tomatoes, basil, 1/8 teaspoon salt and pepper in small bowl.

2. Spray 12-inch nonstick skillet with cooking spray. Heat over medium heat. Cook and stir shrimp, garlic and pepper flakes 3 minutes or until shrimp are opaque. Remove from skillet; set aside.

3. Spray same skillet with cooking spray; heat over medium-high heat. Cook and stir zucchini, onion and remaining 1/4 teaspoon salt 5 minutes or until vegetables edges begin to brown. Add tomato mixture and shrimp to skillet; cook and stir 1 minute until heated through.
Makes 4 servings

Nutrients per Serving: 1-1/3 cups stir-fry

Calories 165	**Fiber** 1g
Fat 5g (sat 25g)	**Cholesterol** 172mg
Protein 24g	**Sodium** 782mg
Carbohydrate 7g	

Exchanges: 1 vegetable, 3 lean meat

Sweet Pepper and Olive Pork

`low carb`

Quick Recipe

     Nonstick cooking spray
  1 pork tenderloin (about 1 pound), cut
       into 1/4-inch slices
1/8 teaspoon salt
1/8 teaspoon black pepper
  2 teaspoons olive oil
  2 medium onions, cut into thin wedges
  2 medium green bell peppers, cut into
       thin bite-size strips
1/2 cup sliced mushrooms
  2 teaspoons minced garlic
1/2 teaspoon ground cumin
1/3 cup chopped pimiento-stuffed green
       olives

1. Spray large skillet with cooking spray; heat over medium-high heat. Season pork slices with salt and pepper. Cook pork in batches 3 minutes or until browned and juices run clear, turning once. Remove pork from skillet; keep warm.

2. Add oil to skillet; heat over medium-high heat. Cook and stir onions, peppers, mushrooms, garlic and cumin 4 minutes or until crisp-tender. Stir in olives; heat through. Serve vegetable mixture with pork slices.

Makes 4 servings

Nutrients per Serving: 3 ounces pork (cooked weight) with 3/4 cup vegetable mixture

Calories 207	**Fiber** 3g
Fat 8g (sat 2g)	**Cholesterol** 63mg
Protein 24g	**Sodium** 330mg
Carbohydrate 10g	

Exchanges: 2 vegetable, 3 lean meat

Tip

Lean pork is a terrific source of protein, B vitamins and zinc.

Tomato Fennel Braised Chicken

`high fiber`

  1 tablespoon olive oil
  4 boneless, skinless chicken breasts (4 to
       5 ounces each)
  2 medium bulbs fennel, cut into 2-inch
       wedges
  2 tablespoons thinly sliced garlic
  1 pound plum tomatoes, quartered and
       seeded
  1 cup California Ripe Olives, whole,
       pitted
  1 cup low-sodium chicken broth
1/2 cup white wine
  1 tablespoon chopped rosemary
     Salt and pepper to taste (optional)

1. Preheat oven to 400°F. Heat oil in a large, high-sided ovenproof skillet over medium-high heat. Add chicken and brown for 3 to 4 minutes on each side. Transfer to a clean plate. Add fennel to skillet and brown for 3 to 4 minutes or until golden. Add garlic and cook for 1 to 2 minutes.

2. Return chicken to pan. Add tomatoes, California Ripe Olives, broth, wine and rosemary. Bring to a boil. Season with salt and pepper to taste, if using. Cover and place in oven for 15 minutes or until cooked through.

Makes 4 servings

Favorite recipe from **California Olive Industry**

Nutrients per Serving: 1 chicken breast with 2 cups fennel mixture

Calories 289	**Fiber** 6g
Fat 9g (sat 1g)	**Cholesterol** 72mg
Protein 30g	**Sodium** 517mg
Carbohydrate 18g	

Exchanges: 1 starch, 4 lean meat

Chili Beef and Corn Casserole

Chili Beef and Corn Casserole

(Pictured above)

Nonstick cooking spray
3/4 pound 95% lean ground beef
1/4 cup salsa
2 teaspoons chili powder
1-1/2 teaspoons ground cumin
2 cups frozen corn kernels, thawed
2 ounces chopped collard greens, about
1/2-inch pieces (1 cup packed)
1/4 cup (1 ounce) shredded reduced-fat
sharp cheddar cheese
1/2 cup fat-free sour cream

1. Preheat oven to 350°F.

2. Spray 12-inch nonstick skillet with cooking spray. Brown beef 6 to 8 minutes over medium-high heat, stirring to break up meat. Drain fat. Add salsa, chili powder and cumin; cook and stir 1 minute. Remove from heat.

3. Spray 9-inch square baking pan with cooking spray. Place corn and collard greens in bottom of pan; toss to blend. Spoon beef mixture evenly over vegetables; cover tightly with foil. Bake 25 minutes or until greens are tender.

4. Top each serving with 1 tablespoon shredded cheese and 2 tablespoons sour cream.

Makes 4 servings

Nutrients per Serving: 1 cup casserole

Calories 254	**Fiber** 3g
Fat 7g (sat 3g)	**Cholesterol** 61mg
Protein 25g	**Sodium** 214mg
Carbohydrate 25g	

Exchanges: 1-1/2 starch, 1/2 vegetable, 2-1/2 lean meat

Chicken with Mango-Cherry Chutney

low fat

Quick Recipe

1-1/2 cups chopped fresh mangoes (about 1-1/2 mangoes), divided
1/3 cup dried tart cherries
1 tablespoon packed brown sugar
1 tablespoon cider vinegar
1/2 teaspoon mustard seeds, slightly crushed
1/4 teaspoon salt, divided
1/4 cup sliced green onions
1-1/2 teaspoons Chinese 5-spice powder
4 boneless skinless chicken breasts *or* 8 small boneless skinless chicken thighs (about 1 pound total)

1. Spray cold grill grid with nonstick cooking spray. Prepare grill for direct grilling.

2. Combine 1/2 cup mango, cherries, brown sugar, vinegar, mustard seeds and 1/8 teaspoon salt in medium saucepan; cook and stir over medium-low heat 5 minutes or until mango is tender. Slightly mash mango. Stir in remaining 1 cup mango and onions. Keep warm.

3. Lightly sprinkle 5-spice powder and remaining 1/8 teaspoon salt on both sides of chicken. Grill chicken directly over medium heat 7 to 10 minutes or until chicken is no longer pink in center, turning once.

4. Serve mango chutney over chicken.
Makes 4 servings

Nutrients per Serving: 1 chicken breast with 2/3 cup chutney

Calories 189	**Fiber** 2g
Fat 3g (sat 1g)	**Cholesterol** 63mg
Protein 24g	**Sodium** 207mg
Carbohydrate 15g	

Exchanges: 1 fruit, 3-1/2 lean meat

Overstuffed Peppers, Mexican Style

Nonstick cooking spray
10 ounces 95% lean ground beef
1/2 cup finely chopped onion
1 can (4 ounces) chopped mild green chiles
1/2 cup frozen corn kernels
1/4 cup cornmeal
1/2 cup tomato sauce, divided
1/2 teaspoon ground cumin
1/2 teaspoon salt
2 large green bell peppers, halved lengthwise, stemmed and seeded
1/2 cup (2 ounces) shredded reduced-fat sharp cheddar cheese

1. Preheat oven to 375°F.

2. Spray medium nonstick skillet with cooking spray; heat over medium-high heat. Brown beef, stirring to separate meat. Drain fat. Add onion, chiles, corn, cornmeal, 1/4 cup tomato sauce, cumin and salt. Mix well.

3. Arrange peppers, cut side up, in 11×7-inch baking pan. Divide beef mixture evenly among pepper halves. Top each stuffed pepper with 1 tablespoon tomato sauce. (Pepper halves will be very full.) Bake, uncovered, 35 minutes or until peppers are tender.

4. Sprinkle each pepper half with 2 tablespoons cheese.
Makes 4 servings

Nutrients per Serving: 1 stuffed pepper half

Calories 232	**Fiber** 4g
Fat 8g (sat 5g)	**Cholesterol** 36mg
Protein 21g	**Sodium** 704mg
Carbohydrate 19g	

Exchanges: 1 starch, 1 vegetable, 2 lean meat, 1/2 fat

Potato and Pork Frittata

(Pictured at right)

12 ounces (about 3 cups) frozen hash
    brown potatoes
1 teaspoon Cajun seasoning
4 egg whites
2 eggs
1/4 cup low-fat (1%) milk
1 teaspoon ground mustard
1/4 teaspoon black pepper
1 package (10 ounces) frozen stir-fry
    vegetable blend
1/3 cup water
3/4 cup chopped cooked lean pork
1/2 cup (2 ounces) shredded reduced-fat
    cheddar cheese

1. Preheat oven to 400°F. Spray baking sheet with nonstick cooking spray. Spread potatoes on baking sheet; sprinkle with Cajun seasoning. Bake 15 minutes or until hot. Remove from oven. *Reduce oven temperature to 350°F.*

2. Beat egg whites, eggs, milk, mustard and pepper in small bowl. Combine vegetables and water in large ovenproof nonstick skillet. Cook over medium heat 5 minutes or until vegetables are crisp-tender; drain.

3. Add pork and potatoes to vegetables in skillet; stir lightly. Add egg mixture. Sprinkle with cheese. Cook over medium-low heat 5 minutes. Place skillet in 350°F oven and bake 5 minutes or until egg mixture is set and cheese is melted. Cut into 4 wedges.

Makes 4 servings

Nutrients per Serving: 1 frittata wedge

Calories 268	**Fiber** 2g
Fat 11g (sat 5g)	**Cholesterol** 145mg
Protein 22g	**Sodium** 258mg
Carbohydrate 20g	

Exchanges: 1-1/2 starch, 2 lean meat, 1 fat

Asparagus and Cheddar Stuffed Chicken Breasts

low carb

20 asparagus spears (about 2 bunches),
    trimmed
2 cups fat-free reduced-sodium chicken
    broth
1 medium red bell pepper, chopped
1/2 teaspoon minced garlic
1 teaspoon dried parsley flakes
1/4 teaspoon black pepper
4 boneless skinless chicken breasts (about
    1/4 pound each)
1/4 cup (1 ounce) shredded reduced-fat
    cheddar cheese
4 tablespoons corn relish (optional)

1. Cut off asparagus tips about 4 inches long; set aside. Slice asparagus stalks; combine with broth, red pepper, garlic, parsley and black pepper in saucepan. Bring to a boil. Reduce heat; simmer, uncovered, 10 to 12 minutes.

2. Meanwhile, place each chicken breast half between 2 pieces of plastic wrap and pound with meat mallet or rolling pin until 1/4 inch thick.

3. Preheat electric indoor grill with lid. Lay 5 asparagus tips across one end of each chicken breast half. Top each with 1 tablespoon cheese; fold in half. Place stuffed breasts on grill and cook with lid closed 6 minutes or until no longer pink.

4. Spoon vegetable sauce evenly onto serving plates and top with stuffed chicken breasts. Garnish with corn relish, if desired.

Makes 4 servings

Nutrients per Serving: 1 stuffed chicken breast and 1/4 of sauce

Calories 189	**Fiber** 2g
Fat 4g (sat 2g)	**Cholesterol** 83mg
Protein 33g	**Sodium** 317mg
Carbohydrate 5g	

Exchanges: 1 vegetable, 4 lean meat

Potato and Pork Frittata

Roasted Almond Tilapia

Roasted Almond Tilapia

Quick Recipe   *(Pictured above)*

>   2 tilapia fillets or Boston scrod fish fillets
>   (6 ounces each)
>   1/4 teaspoon salt
>   1 tablespoon coarse-grained mustard
>   1/4 cup fresh whole wheat bread crumbs
>   (1/2 slice bread)
>   2 tablespoons chopped almonds
>   Lemon wedges (optional)

1. Heat oven to 450°F. Place fish on small baking sheet. Season with salt. Spread mustard over fish. Combine bread crumbs and almonds; sprinkle over fish.

2. Bake 8 to 10 minutes or until fish is opaque in center and flakes when tested with fork. Serve with lemon wedges.   *Makes 2 servings*

Serving Suggestion: Serve with steamed vegetables.

Nutrients per Serving: 1 fillet

Calories 268	**Fiber** 2g
Fat 10g (sat <1g)	**Cholesterol** 0mg
Protein 32g	**Sodium** 587mg
Carbohydrate 14g	

Exchanges: 1/2 starch, 4 lean meat

Smothered Salisbury Steak

low carb

Quick Recipe

>   2 teaspoons olive oil
>   1 large Vidalia onion, thinly sliced
>   1/2 teaspoon salt, divided
>   3/8 teaspoon ground black pepper, divided
>   1 pound 95% lean ground beef
>   1/2 cup fresh whole wheat bread crumbs
>   (1 slice bread)
>   1 clove garlic, minced
>   1 egg white
>   1 tablespoon Worcestershire sauce
>   1/2 cup fat-free beef gravy, heated

1. Heat oil in large nonstick skillet over medium-high heat. Add onion; cover and cook 3 minutes or until onion is crisp-tender. Sprinkle with 1/4 teaspoon salt and 1/8 teaspoon pepper. Cook, stirring frequently, over medium heat 3 minutes or until onion is golden brown. Cover; keep warm.

2. Meanwhile, combine beef, bread crumbs, garlic, egg white, Worcestershire sauce, remaining 1/4 teaspoon salt and 1/4 teaspoon pepper. Mix lightly but thoroughly; shape into 4 (1/2-inch-thick) oval patties.

3. Remove onion from skillet; set aside. Add patties to skillet; cook over medium heat 6 to 7 minutes per side or until internal temperature reaches 160°F. Transfer to serving plates; top with gravy and reserved onions.

Makes 4 servings

Nutrients per Serving: 1 patty with 3 tablespoons onion mixture and 2 tablespoons gravy

Calories 215	**Fiber** <1g
Fat 8g (sat 2g)	**Cholesterol** 66mg
Protein 27g	**Sodium** 585mg
Carbohydrate 8g	

Exchanges: 1/2 starch, 3-1/2 lean meat

Vegetable Fajitas with Spicy Salsa

(Pictured on page 64)

Spicy Salsa

- 3 whole medium tomatoes
- 1 small onion, unpeeled
- 1 jalapeño pepper
- 6 cloves garlic, unpeeled
  Juice of 1 lime

Fajitas

- 12 (8-inch) flour tortillas
- 1 tablespoon canola oil
- 4 medium bell peppers, cut into strips
- 1 medium red onion, peeled, halved lengthwise and thickly sliced
- 1/8 teaspoon salt (optional)
  Black pepper (optional)
- 1 can (16 ounces) vegetarian refried beans
  Chopped cilantro and fat-free sour cream (optional)

1. For salsa, preheat broiler. Line baking sheet with foil. Place unpeeled tomatoes, onion, jalapeño and garlic on prepared baking sheet; broil 10 minutes. Turn vegetables and rotate pan. Broil 10 minutes more or until blackened. Cool 10 minutes. Peel tomatoes, onion and garlic; peel and seed jalapeño. Place in blender or food processor with lime juice and salt; process until desired consistency. Refrigerate. (Can be made up to 1 week in advance.)

2. For fajitas, heat large cast iron or heavy skillet over medium-high heat until hot. Heat tortillas, one at a time, until browned, about 15 seconds per side; keep warm.

3. Reduce heat to medium. Add oil. Add pepper strips and red onion slices; sprinkle with salt and pepper, if desired. Cook, stirring occasionally, about 10 minutes or until onion is cooked through and peppers are crisp-tender.

4. Heat refried beans in small saucepan over medium heat. Spread about 2 tablespoons beans evenly over each tortilla. Top with 1/3 cup vegetables and 2 tablespoons salsa. Roll up; serve immediately. Garnish with cilantro and sour cream, if desired.

Makes 6 servings

Nutrients per Serving: 2 fajitas

Calories 292	**Fiber** 6g
Fat 7g (sat 1g)	**Cholesterol** 0mg
Protein 9g	**Sodium** 781mg
Carbohydrate 49g	

Exchanges: 2-1/2 starch, 2 vegetable, 1 fat

Asian Inspired Pork & Nectarine Kabobs

- 1 pork tenderloin (about 1 pound)
- 3/4 cup pineapple juice
- 3 tablespoons reduced-sodium soy sauce
- 1 tablespoon grated fresh ginger
- 1 teaspoon minced garlic
- 1 teaspoon ground cumin
- 1 teaspoon chili powder
- 1/2 teaspoon black pepper
- 3 fresh medium nectarines

1. Cut pork tenderloin in half lengthwise. Cut each half into 8 pieces (16 pieces total). Place pork in resealable food storage bag. Place bag in shallow dish.

2. Stir together pineapple juice, soy sauce, ginger, garlic, cumin, chili powder and pepper. Pour over pork; seal bag. Marinate in refrigerator 3 to 6 hours.

3. Spray cold grill grid with nonstick cooking spray. Prepare grill for direct grilling.

4. Cut each nectarine into 8 chunks. Drain pork, discarding marinade. Thread pork and nectarine pieces onto 8 short skewers. Grill over medium heat 9 to 12 minutes until pork is no longer pink in center, turning once. *Makes 4 servings*

Nutrients per Serving: 2 skewers

Calories 211	**Fiber** 2g
Fat 4g (sat 1g)	**Cholesterol** 67mg
Protein 25g	**Sodium** 429mg
Carbohydrate 20g	

Exchanges: 1 fruit, 3 lean meat

Rosemary-Garlic Scallops with Polenta

Quick Recipe   *(Pictured at right)*

> 2 teaspoons olive oil
> 1 medium red bell pepper, seeded and sliced
> 1/3 cup chopped red onion
> 3 cloves garlic, minced
> 1/2 pound fresh bay scallops
> 2 teaspoons chopped fresh rosemary *or* 3/4 teaspoon dried rosemary
> 1/4 teaspoon black pepper
> 1-1/4 cups fat-free reduced-sodium chicken broth
> 1/2 cup cornmeal
> 1/4 teaspoon salt

1. Heat oil in large nonstick skillet over medium heat. Add bell pepper, onion and garlic. Cook and stir 5 minutes. Add scallops, rosemary and black pepper. Cook 3 to 5 minutes or until scallops are opaque, stirring occasionally.

2. Meanwhile, combine broth, cornmeal and salt in small saucepan. Bring to a boil over high heat. Reduce heat to low; simmer 5 minutes or until polenta is very thick, stirring frequently. Transfer to two serving plates. Top polenta with scallop mixture.   *Makes 2 servings*

Nutrients per Serving: 1-3/4 cups

Calories 304	**Fiber** 4g
Fat 8g (sat 1g)	**Cholesterol** 53mg
Protein 26g	**Sodium** 731mg
Carbohydrate 33g	

Exchanges: 2 starch, 3 lean meat

Southwestern Tortilla Stack

> 2 cans (about 16 ounces each) vegetarian refried beans
> 1/2 cup reduced-fat sour cream
> 1 can (4 ounces) chopped mild green chiles, drained (optional)
> 1/2 teaspoon ground cumin
> 3 (10-inch) flour tortillas
> 1 cup (4 ounces) shredded reduced-fat cheddar cheese
> Salsa (optional)

1. Preheat oven to 425°F. Spray 10-inch round casserole with nonstick cooking spray.

2. Combine beans, sour cream, chiles and cumin in medium bowl.

3. Place one tortilla in bottom of prepared casserole. Top with half of bean mixture and 1/3 cup cheese. Top with second tortilla; repeat layers of beans and cheese.

4. Cover with remaining tortilla; sprinkle with remaining cheese.

5. Cover; bake 20 minutes or until heated through. Cut into wedges. Serve with salsa, if desired.   *Makes 6 servings*

Nutrients per Serving: 1 wedge (1/6 of total recipe)

Calories 355	**Fiber** 10g
Fat 9g (sat 5g)	**Cholesterol** 24mg
Protein 20g	**Sodium** 988mg
Carbohydrate 50g	

Exchanges: 3-1/2 starch, 1-1/2 lean meat, 1 fat

Rosemary-Garlic Scallops with Polenta

Turkey-Tortilla Bake

Quick Recipe   *(Pictured at right)*

- **9 (6-inch) corn tortillas**
- **1/2 pound 93% lean ground turkey**
- **1/2 cup chopped onion**
- **3/4 cup mild or medium taco sauce**
- **1 can (4 ounces) chopped mild green chiles, drained**
- **1/2 cup frozen corn, thawed**
- **1/2 cup (2 ounces) shredded reduced-fat cheddar cheese**

1. Preheat oven to 400°F. Place tortillas on large baking sheet, overlapping as little as possible. Bake 4 minutes. Turn tortillas over; bake 2 minutes or until crisp. Cool completely on wire rack.

2. Heat medium nonstick skillet over medium heat. Cook ground turkey and onion until turkey is no longer pink and onion is tender, stirring to separate meat. Add taco sauce, chiles and corn. Reduce heat; simmer 5 minutes.

3. Break 3 tortillas and arrange over bottom of 1-1/2-quart casserole. Spoon half of turkey mixture over tortillas; sprinkle with 1/4 cup cheese. Repeat layers. Bake 10 minutes or until cheese is melted and casserole is heated through. Break remaining 3 tortillas into pieces and sprinkle over casserole.

Makes 4 servings

Nutrients per Serving: 1 cup casserole

Calories 279	**Fiber** 1g
Fat 8g (sat 2g)	**Cholesterol** 26mg
Protein 17g	**Sodium** 666mg
Carbohydrate 38g	

Exchanges: 2-1/2 starch, 2 lean meat, 1 fat

Orange-Glazed Pork Chops with Butternut Squash & Cranberries

Quick Recipe

- **2 teaspoons olive oil**
- **3 cups cubed peeled butternut squash**
- **1/4 cup orange juice**
- **4 tablespoons reduced-sugar orange marmalade, divided**
- **1/4 cup dried cranberries**
  Nonstick cooking spray
- **4 boneless center-cut pork chops (about 1/4 pound each), trimmed of fat**
- **1/4 teaspoon salt**
- **1/4 teaspoon black pepper**

1. Heat oil in large nonstick skillet over medium heat. Add squash; cook, covered, stirring occasionally, 15 minutes or until tender. Stir in orange juice, 2 tablespoons orange marmalade and cranberries. Cook, uncovered, 1 minute or until almost all liquid evaporates.

2. Meanwhile, spray large nonstick heavy skillet with cooking spray; heat over medium-high heat. Sprinkle pork chops with salt and pepper; cook 3 to 4 minutes per side or until meat thermometer reads 160°F.

3. Add remaining 2 tablespoons marmalade; as marmalade melts, turn chops until coated. Serve pork with squash.   *Makes 4 servings*

Nutrients per Serving: 1 pork chop with 1/2 cup squash mixture

Calories 265	**Fiber** 2g
Fat 8g (sat 2g)	**Cholesterol** 71mg
Protein 26g	**Sodium** 209mg
Carbohydrate 23g	

Exchanges: 1-1/2 starch, 3 lean meat

Spicy Peanut-Coconut Shrimp

Quick Recipe   (Pictured at right)

- **1/4 cup shredded coconut**
- **2 teaspoons dark sesame oil**
- **1 pound uncooked large raw shrimp (thawed if frozen), peeled, deveined and patted dry**
- **1/4 to 1/2 teaspoon crushed red pepper flakes**
- **2 tablespoons chopped fresh mint or cilantro**
- **1/4 cup chopped lightly salted roasted peanuts**
- **Fresh lime wedges**

1. Toast coconut in small nonstick skillet over medium-high heat 2 to 3 minutes until golden, stirring constantly. Immediately remove from skillet.

2. Heat oil in large nonstick skillet over medium-high heat. Add shrimp and pepper flakes; stir-fry 3 to 4 minutes until shrimp are pink and opaque. Add mint; toss well and transfer to serving plates. Top each serving with 1 tablespoon toasted coconut and 1 tablespoon chopped peanuts. Garnish with lime wedges.

Makes 4 servings

Serving Suggestion: Serve with steamed sugar snap peas and whole wheat couscous.

Nutrients per Serving: 3/4 cup shrimp mixture

Calories 212	**Fiber** 1g
Fat 10g (sat 3g)	**Cholesterol** 172mg
Protein 25g	**Sodium** 243mg
Carbohydrate 4g	

Exchanges: 3-1/2 lean meat

Tofu, Vegetable and Curry Stir-Fry

- **1 package (about 14 ounces) extra-firm reduced-fat tofu**
- **3/4 cup reduced-fat coconut milk**
- **2 tablespoons fresh lime juice**
- **1 tablespoon curry powder**
- **2 teaspoons dark sesame oil, divided**
- **4 cups broccoli florets (1-1/2-inch pieces)**
- **2 medium red bell peppers, cut into short, thin strips**
- **1 medium red onion, cut into thin wedges**
- **1/4 teaspoon salt**
- **Hot cooked brown rice (optional)**

1. Place tofu on several layers of paper towels. Cover with additional paper towels and weigh it down with heavy plate. Let stand 15 to 20 minutes; cut into 3/4-inch cubes. Set aside. Combine coconut milk, lime juice and curry powder in medium bowl; set aside.

2. Heat 1 teaspoon oil in large nonstick skillet over medium heat. Add tofu; cook, turning cubes often, 10 minutes or until lightly browned on all sides. Remove to plate; set aside. Add remaining 1 teaspoon oil to same skillet; increase heat to high.

3. Add broccoli, bell peppers and onion; stir-fry about 5 minutes or until vegetables are crisp-tender. Stir in tofu and coconut milk mixture; bring to a boil, stirring frequently. Stir in salt. Serve immediately with rice, if desired.

Makes 4 servings

Nutrients per Serving: about 2 cups stir-fry

Calories 191	**Fiber** 6g
Fat 9g (sat 2g)	**Cholesterol** 0mg
Protein 14g	**Sodium** 192mg
Carbohydrate 16g	

Exchanges: 4 vegetable, 1 lean meat, 1 fat

Spicy Peanut-Coconut Shrimp

Fast Catfish in Foil

Fast Catfish in Foil

(Pictured above)

4 catfish fillets (4 ounces each)

2 cups shredded carrots

6 ounces green beans, ends trimmed (about 60 beans)

8 unpeeled baby red potatoes, thinly sliced

Nonstick cooking spray

4 teaspoons lemon juice

2 teaspoons dried parsley flakes

1 teaspoon black pepper

1. Preheat oven to 425°F. Place one fillet, skin side down, on each of 4 (12×12-inch) sheets of foil. Top each fillet with 1/2 cup shredded carrots, 15 green beans and 2 sliced potatoes.

2. Spray ingredients on each foil square with cooking spray. Sprinkle each with 1 teaspoon lemon juice, 1/2 teaspoon parsley flakes and 1/4 teaspoon pepper.

3. Double fold sides and ends of foil to seal packets, leaving head space for heat circulation. Place packets on baking sheet. Bake 30 minutes.

4. Remove packets from oven; let stand 5 minutes. Carefully open packets, allowing steam to escape. Fish should flake when tested with fork. Serve immediately.

Makes 4 servings

Nutrients per Serving: 1 foil packet

Calories 227	**Fiber** 5g
Fat 3g (sat <1g)	**Cholesterol** 65mg
Protein 22g	**Sodium** 97mg
Carbohydrate 28g	

Exchanges: 1 starch, 2 vegetable, 3 lean meat

Beef Kabobs with Parmesan Orzo

Quick Recipe

  1 pound boneless beef top sirloin steak, cut 1 inch thick

  2 red or yellow bell peppers, cut into 1-inch pieces

  1 tablespoon chopped fresh basil or 1 teaspoon dried basil

  1 tablespoon prepared Italian dressing

  2 large cloves garlic, minced

Parmesan Orzo

  1 cup uncooked orzo pasta, cooked

  2 to 3 tablespoons chopped fresh basil or parsley

  2 tablespoons shredded Parmesan cheese

  2 teaspoons olive oil

1. Soak eight 8-inch bamboo skewers in water 10 minutes.

2. Cut beef steak into 1-1/4-inch pieces. Toss beef and bell peppers with 1 tablespoon basil, dressing and garlic in large bowl. Alternately thread beef and peppers onto skewers.

3. Toss orzo ingredients in medium bowl; keep warm.

4. Place kabobs on grid over medium, ash-covered coals. Grill, uncovered, about 8 to 10 minutes for medium rare to medium doneness, turning occasionally. Serve with orzo.
Makes 4 servings

Favorite recipe from **National Cattlemen's Beef Association on behalf of The Beef Checkoff**

Nutrients per Serving: 2 kabobs with about 2/3 cup cooked orzo

Calories 410	**Fiber** 3g
Fat 12g (sat 4g)	**Cholesterol** 56mg
Protein 33g	**Sodium** 160mg
Carbohydrate 42g	

Exchanges: 2-1/2 starch, 1 vegetable, 3-1/2 lean meat

Mushroom & Chicken Skillet

Quick Recipe

  1 pound boneless skinless chicken breasts, cut into bite-size pieces

  1 can (about 14 ounces) fat-free reduced-sodium chicken broth

  1/4 cup hot water

  1/2 teaspoon dried thyme

  2 cups uncooked instant rice

  8 ounces mushrooms, thinly sliced

  1 can (10-3/4 ounces) condensed 98% fat-free cream of celery soup, undiluted

1. Place chicken, chicken broth and water in 12-inch nonstick skillet; cook over medium-high heat until chicken is no longer pink. Stir in rice and thyme, making sure rice is covered with broth. Bring to a boil. Place mushrooms on top. Cover skillet; turn off heat and let stand 5 minutes.

2. Add soup; cook and stir over low heat 2 minutes until well blended and heated through.
Makes 4 servings

Nutrients per Serving: 1-1/2 cups

Calories 277	**Fiber** 2g
Fat 4g (sat 1g)	**Cholesterol** 67mg
Protein 32g	**Sodium** 774mg
Carbohydrate 28g	

Exchanges: 2 starch, 3 lean meat

Tip

Skillet dishes are a fast and easy way to make a meal. They require just a few ingredients and use only one pan, making cleanup a breeze and leaving plenty of time to enjoy your meal.

Seared Chicken with Greek Salsa

Quick Recipe   *(Pictured at right)*

Salsa

> 1 small cucumber, seeded and chopped (about 1 cup total)
> 3 tablespoons chopped fresh mint
> 2 tablespoons finely chopped red onion
> 1 to 2 tablespoons lemon juice
> 1/2 to 3/4 teaspoon grated lemon peel
> 1/8 teaspoon salt
> 1/8 teaspoon red pepper flakes (optional)
> 1/4 cup (1 ounce) crumbled feta with sun-dried tomatoes and basil

Chicken

> 4 boneless skinless chicken breasts (about 1/4 pound each)
> 3/4 teaspoon dried oregano
> 1/4 teaspoon salt
> 1/4 teaspoon black pepper
> Nonstick cooking spray

1. Combine all salsa ingredients except feta in medium bowl. Toss gently to blend; set aside.

2. Season both sides of chicken with oregano, salt and pepper.

3. Heat large nonstick skillet over medium-high heat until hot. Coat both sides of chicken with cooking spray. Cook 5 minutes on each side or until cooked through.

4. Add feta to salsa; toss gently. Serve with chicken.   *Makes 4 servings*

Serving Suggestion: Serve with hot couscous tossed with green onion and steamed asparagus.

Nutrients per Serving: 1 chicken breast with 1/3 cup salsa

Calories 153	**Fiber** <1g
Fat 3g (sat 1g)	**Cholesterol** 71mg
Protein 28g	**Sodium** 357mg
Carbohydrate 3g	

Exchanges: 3 lean meat

Pasta with Italian Sausage & Broccoli

Quick Recipe

> 8 ounces (2 cups) uncooked whole wheat rotini
> 1 pound lean mild or hot Italian turkey sausage
> 1 medium onion, cut into wedges
> 2 cloves garlic, minced
> 1/4 teaspoon red pepper flakes (optional)
> 5 cups broccoli florets
> 1/2 cup fat-free reduced-sodium chicken broth
> 1/2 cup plus 2 tablespoons grated Parmesan cheese, divided
> 1/2 teaspoon black pepper

1. Cook pasta according to package directions, omitting salt; drain. Transfer to large serving bowl; keep warm.

2. Meanwhile, remove sausage from casings; crumble into large nonstick skillet. Brown sausage over medium heat, stirring to separate meat. Drain fat.

3. Add onion; cook and stir 3 minutes. Stir in garlic and red pepper flakes, if desired; cook and stir 1 minute. Add broccoli and broth; cover and cook 4 to 6 minutes or until meat is no longer pink and broccoli is crisp-tender. Add onion mixture to hot pasta. Sprinkle with 1/2 cup cheese and pepper; toss until blended. Sprinkle each serving with 1 teaspoon cheese.   *Makes 6 servings*

Nutrients per Serving: 1-1/2 cups

Calories 320	**Fiber** 5g
Fat 11g (sat 3g)	**Cholesterol** 52mg
Protein 23g	**Sodium** 671mg
Carbohydrate 35g	

Exchanges: 2 starch, 1 vegetable, 2 lean meat, 1/2 fat

Seared Chicken with Greek Salsa

Szechwan Pork Stir-Fry over Spinach

Szechwan Pork Stir-Fry over Spinach

cooking for 1 or 2

Quick Recipe   *(Pictured above)*

  2 teaspoons sesame oil, divided
  3/4 cup matchstick-size carrot strips
  1/2 pound pork tenderloin, halved lengthwise and thinly sliced
  3 cloves garlic, minced
  2 teaspoons minced ginger
  1/4 to 1/2 teaspoon red pepper flakes
  1 tablespoon reduced-sodium soy sauce
  1 tablespoon mirin* or dry sherry
  2 teaspoons cornstarch
  8 ounces baby spinach leaves
  2 teaspoons sesame seeds, toasted**

*Mirin, a sweet wine made from rice, is an essential flavoring in Japanese cuisine. It is available in Asian markets and the Asian or gourmet section of some supermarkets.

**To toast sesame seeds, spread in large, dry skillet. Shake skillet over medium-low heat about 3 minutes or until seeds begin to pop and turn golden.

1. Heat 1 teaspoon oil in large nonstick skillet over medium-high heat. Add carrot strips. Cook 3 minutes, stirring occasionally. Add pork, garlic, ginger and red pepper flakes. Stir-fry 3 minutes or until pork is no longer pink. Combine soy sauce, mirin and cornstarch in small bowl. Add to pork mixture. Stir-fry about 1 minute or until sauce thickens.

2. Heat remaining 1 teaspoon oil in medium saucepan over medium-high heat. Add spinach. Cover and cook 1 minute. Uncover and turn spinach with tongs. Cover and cook until spinach is barely wilted, about 1 minute. Transfer spinach to 2 serving plates. Spoon pork mixture over spinach. Top with sesame seeds.

Makes 2 servings

Nutrients per Serving: 2 cups

Calories 256	**Fiber** 3g
Fat 10g (sat 2g)	**Cholesterol** 73mg
Protein 29g	**Sodium** 466mg
Carbohydrate 11g	

Exchanges: 2 vegetable, 4 lean meat

Chicken Picadillo

`low fat` `low carb`

Quick Recipe

  1 pound boneless skinless chicken breasts
  1 teaspoon ground cumin
  Nonstick cooking spray
  3/4 cup thick-and-chunky salsa
  1/2 teaspoon chopped garlic
  1 medium onion, sliced
  1 medium green bell pepper, sliced

1. Cut chicken into 1-inch strips. Sprinkle with cumin.

2. Spray large skillet with cooking spray. Cook chicken 10 minutes over medium-high heat or until cooked through. Add salsa, garlic, onion and bell pepper. Cover; simmer 10 minutes or until vegetables are tender.

Makes 4 servings

Nutrients per Serving: 1 cup

Calories 149	**Fiber** 1g
Fat 2g (sat <1g)	**Cholesterol** 66mg
Protein 27g	**Sodium** 317mg
Carbohydrate 5g	

Exchanges: 1 vegetable, 3 lean meat

Roast Salmon with Lentils & Squash

Nonstick cooking spray
3/4 cup dried brown lentils, rinsed and sorted
2 cups water
1 tablespoon plus 1-1/2 teaspoons refrigerated basil pesto
1/4 teaspoon grated lemon peel
2 tablespoons fresh lemon juice
1 salmon fillet (1 pound, 1-1/2 inches thick)
1/4 teaspoon salt
1/4 teaspoon black pepper, divided
1 medium red bell pepper, diced
1 small onion, coarsely chopped
1 medium yellow summer squash, diced

1. Preheat oven to 400°F. Line shallow baking pan with foil. Spray foil with cooking spray. Combine lentils and water in medium saucepan. Bring to a boil. Reduce heat; simmer, uncovered, 15 to 18 minutes or until lentils are just tender. Drain.

2. Meanwhile, combine pesto, lemon peel and lemon juice in small bowl; mix well. Set aside.

3. Sprinkle salmon with salt and 1/8 teaspoon black pepper. Place in prepared baking pan. Bake 10 minutes or until fish just begins to flake when tested with fork.

4. Meanwhile, spray large nonstick skillet with cooking spray. Heat over medium heat until hot. Add bell pepper and onion; cook and stir 3 minutes. Add squash; cook, stirring frequently, about 5 minutes or until crisp-tender. Stir in lentils, 1 tablespoon pesto mixture and remaining 1/8 teaspoon black pepper. Cut salmon into 4 equal pieces. Place salmon on plates; drizzle each serving with remaining 1 teaspoon pesto mixture. Serve with lentil mixture. *Makes 4 servings*

Nutrients per Serving: 1 piece of salmon with about 1 cup lentil mixture

Calories 406	**Fiber** 14g
Fat 16g (sat 3g)	**Cholesterol** 69mg
Protein 35g	**Sodium** 581mg
Carbohydrate 31g	

Exchanges: 2 starch, 4 lean meat, 1 fat

Beef & Vegetable Skillet

Quick Recipe

1-1/4 pounds boneless beef top sirloin steak, cut 3/4 inch thick
2 teaspoons dark sesame oil
2 garlic cloves, minced
1 medium red bell pepper, cut into thin strips
3 tablespoons reduced-sodium soy sauce, divided
2 tablespoons water
3 cups coarsely chopped fresh spinach
1/2 cup sliced green onions
3 tablespoons ketchup
2 cups hot cooked rice, prepared without butter or salt

1. Cut beef steak lengthwise in half and then crosswise into 1/4-inch strips. Toss with sesame oil and garlic.

2. Heat large nonstick skillet over medium-high heat until hot. Add beef (1/2 at a time); stir-fry 1 to 2 minutes or until outside surface is no longer pink. Remove from skillet.

3. In same skillet, add bell pepper, 2 tablespoons soy sauce and water. Cook 2 to 3 minutes or until pepper is crisp-tender. Add spinach and green onions; cook until spinach is just wilted. Stir in ketchup, 1 tablespoon soy sauce and beef; heat through. Serve over rice.

Makes 4 servings

Favorite recipe from **National Cattlemen's Beef Association on behalf of The Beef Checkoff**

Nutrients per Serving: 1 cup beef mixture with 1/2 cup rice

Calories 334	**Fiber** 2g
Fat 9g (sat 3g)	**Cholesterol** 62mg
Protein 36g	**Sodium** 688mg
Carbohydrate 25g	

Exchanges: 1 starch, 2 vegetable, 4 lean meat

Yankee Pot Roast

(Pictured at right)

1 boneless beef chuck pot roast (arm, shoulder or blade), about 2-1/2 pounds
1/3 cup all-purpose flour
3/4 teaspoon salt
3/4 teaspoon pepper
1 tablespoon vegetable oil
1 can (14 to 14-1/2 ounces) beef broth
1/2 cup dry red wine
1-1/2 teaspoons dried thyme leaves, crushed
2 packages (16 ounces each) frozen vegetable stew mixture (such as potatoes, carrots, celery and onion)

1. Combine flour, salt and pepper. Lightly coat beef in 2 tablespoons of the flour mixture. Heat oil in large stockpot over medium heat until hot. Place beef pot roast in stockpot; brown evenly. Pour off drippings.

2. Combine beef broth, red wine, thyme and remaining flour mixture; add to stockpot and bring to a boil. Reduce heat; cover tightly and simmer 2 hours. Add vegetables to stock pot; continue simmering 30 to 45 minutes or until pot roast and vegetables are fork-tender.

3. Remove pot roast and vegetables; keep warm. Skim fat from cooking liquid, if necessary.

4. Carve pot roast into pieces. Serve with vegetables and gravy.   *Makes 6 servings*

Favorite recipe from **National Cattlemen's Beef Association on behalf of The Beef Checkoff**

Nutrients per Serving: 1-1/3 cups beef and vegetables

Calories 363	**Fiber** 1g
Fat 10g (sat 3g)	**Cholesterol** 71mg
Protein 39g	**Sodium** 735mg
Carbohydrate 25g	

Exchanges: 1/2 starch, 3-1/2 vegetable, 4-1/2 lean meat

Tuna Steaks with Tomatoes & Olives

low carb

Quick Recipe

2 teaspoons olive oil
1 small onion, quartered and sliced
1 clove garlic, minced
1-1/3 cups chopped tomatoes
1/4 cup sliced drained black olives
2 anchovy fillets, finely chopped (optional)
2 tablespoons chopped fresh basil
1/4 teaspoon salt, divided
1/8 teaspoon red pepper flakes
4 tuna steaks (about 6 ounces each and 3/4 inch thick)
Black pepper (optional)
Nonstick cooking spray
1/4 cup toasted* pine nuts (optional)

*Spread nuts in shallow baking pan. Bake in preheated 350°F oven 5 to 10 minutes or until fragrant, stirring occasionally.

1. Heat oil in large skillet over medium heat. Add onion; cook and stir 4 minutes. Add garlic; cook and stir about 30 seconds. Add tomatoes; cook 3 minutes, stirring occasionally. Stir in olives, anchovy fillets, if desired, basil, 1/8 teaspoon salt and red pepper flakes. Cook until most of liquid is evaporated.

2. Meanwhile, sprinkle tuna with remaining 1/8 teaspoon salt and black pepper, if desired. Spray another large nonstick skillet with cooking spray; heat over medium-high heat. Cook tuna 2 to 3 minutes on each side or until fish flakes when tested with fork. Serve with tomato mixture. Garnish with pine nuts, if desired.
          Makes 4 servings

Nutrients per Serving: 1 tuna steak with 1/2 cup tomato mixture

Calories 233	**Fiber** 1g
Fat 5g (sat 1g)	**Cholesterol** 77mg
Protein 41g	**Sodium** 288mg
Carbohydrate 5g	

Exchanges: 1 vegetable, 4-1/2 lean meat

Yankee Pot Roast

Turkey Shanghai

low fat

Quick Recipe   *(Pictured at right)*

Nonstick cooking spray
3/4 pound turkey breast tenderloins, thinly sliced
1 cup thinly sliced carrots
1/2 cup sliced green onions
3 cloves garlic, minced
4 cups fat-free reduced-sodium chicken broth
6 ounces uncooked angel hair pasta
2 cups frozen French-style green beans
1/4 cup plus 2 tablespoons stir-fry sauce
1 teaspoon dark sesame oil

1. Spray large nonstick skillet with cooking spray; heat over medium heat until hot. Add turkey and carrots; cook and stir 5 minutes or until turkey is no longer pink. Stir in green onions and garlic; cook and stir 2 minutes.

2. Add chicken broth to skillet; bring to a boil over high heat. Stir in pasta. Return to a boil. Reduce heat to low. Simmer, uncovered, 5 minutes, stirring frequently.

3. Stir in green beans. Simmer, stirring occasionally, 2 to 3 minutes or until pasta is just tender. Remove from heat. Stir in stir-fry sauce and sesame oil. Let stand 5 minutes.

Makes 6 servings

Nutrients per Serving: about 1-1/4 cups

Calories 209	**Fiber** 3g
Fat 3g (sat 1g)	**Cholesterol** 25mg
Protein 20g	**Sodium** 712mg
Carbohydrate 28g	

Exchanges: 1-1/2 starch, 1 vegetable, 1-1/2 lean meat

Pork Chops with Skillet Corn

Quick Recipe

4 boneless pork chops (about 1/4 pound each), trimmed
3/4 teaspoon salt, divided
1/4 to 1/2 teaspoon ground chipotle pepper *or* 1/2 teaspoon chili powder
Nonstick cooking spray
1 cup chopped onion
1 medium red bell pepper, chopped
1 teaspoon olive oil
2 cups frozen corn, thawed and drained
1/4 teaspoon ground cumin

1. Sprinkle both sides of pork chops with 1/2 teaspoon salt and chipotle pepper.

2. Spray large skillet with cooking spray; heat over medium heat until hot. Add pork chops. Cook 4 minutes; turn and cook 3 minutes more or until meat thermometer reads 160°F. Set aside and keep warm.

3. Add onion, bell pepper and oil to same skillet. Cook 4 to 5 minutes, stirring frequently. Add corn, cumin and remaining 1/4 teaspoon salt; cook 1 minute or until onion is tender and corn is heated through.

4. Serve pork chops with corn mixture.

Makes 4 servings

Nutrients per Serving: 1 pork chop with 1/2 cup corn mixture

Calories 269	**Fiber** 3g
Fat 10g (sat 3g)	**Cholesterol** 72mg
Protein 24g	**Sodium** 375mg
Carbohydrate 21g	

Exchanges: 1-1/2 starch, 3 lean meat

Turkey Shanghai

White Bean and Chicken Ragout

White Bean and Chicken Ragout

high fiber **cooking for 1 or 2**

(Pictured above)

- **2 boneless skinless chicken thighs**
- **2 small carrots, cut into 1/2-inch pieces**
- **2 medium celery stalks, cut into 1/2-inch pieces**
- **1/4 medium onion, chopped**
- **1 clove garlic**
- **1 bay leaf**
- **1 sprig parsley**
- **1 sprig thyme**
- **3 black peppercorns**
- **1 cup canned cannellini beans, rinsed and drained**
- **1 plum tomato, chopped**
- **1 teaspoon herbes de Provençe**
- **1/2 teaspoon salt**
- **1/8 teaspoon black pepper**
- **1 teaspoon olive oil**
- **1 tablespoon chopped fresh parsley**
- **Grated peel of 1 lemon**

1. Place chicken thighs in medium saucepan; add cool water to cover. Add carrots, celery, onion, garlic, bay leaf, parsley sprig, thyme and peppercorns; bring to a boil over high heat. Reduce heat; simmer 15 to 20 minutes or until chicken is no longer pink.

2. Remove chicken from saucepan; let cool 5 minutes.

3. Drain vegetables; reserve broth. Discard garlic, bay leaf, parsley, thyme and peppercorns. Return vegetables to saucepan.

4. Cut chicken into bite-size pieces; add to saucepan with vegetables. Stir in beans and tomato. Add herbes de Provençe, salt and pepper.

5. Stir in 1 cup broth; simmer 5 minutes.

6. Divide stew between 2 bowls; drizzle 1/2 teaspoon olive oil over each. Garnish with chopped parsley and lemon peel.

Makes 2 servings

Nutrients per Serving: 1-1/2 cups stew

Calories 283	**Fiber** 10g
Fat 6g (sat <1g)	**Cholesterol** 57mg
Protein 24g	**Sodium** 715mg
Carbohydrate 36g	

Exchanges: 2 starch, 3 lean meat

Tip

Cannellini beans are Italian white beans also known as white kidney beans. They have a very smooth texture, mellow flavor, and maintain their shape well when cooked. Great northern beans can be substituted.

Quick-Braised Chicken Thighs & Vegetables

2 tablespoons all-purpose flour
1 teaspoon dried thyme
1/2 teaspoon salt
1/4 teaspoon black pepper
4 bone-in skinless chicken thighs (1-1/2 to 1-3/4 pounds)
2 teaspoons olive oil
1 cup fat-free reduced-sodium chicken broth
12 ounces fresh green beans, trimmed and cut into 1-inch pieces
1 large red bell pepper, cut into short, thin strips
1/4 cup grated Parmesan cheese

1. Combine flour, thyme, salt and black pepper in large resealable food storage bag. Add chicken, one piece at a time; shake to coat lightly with flour mixture.

2. Heat oil in large deep skillet over medium heat until hot. Place chicken, meat side down, in skillet; sprinkle any remaining flour mixture from bag over chicken. Cook 5 minutes; turn chicken over and add broth to skillet. Simmer, uncovered, 15 minutes, turning once.

3. Add green beans and bell pepper to skillet. Cover; simmer 8 to 10 minutes or until vegetables are tender, chicken is cooked through and juices run clear. Transfer chicken to serving plates. Stir vegetable mixture; serve vegetables over chicken. Sprinkle with cheese.

Makes 4 servings

Nutrients per Serving: 1 chicken thigh with about 1/3 cup vegetable mixture

Calories 178	**Fiber** 3g
Fat 7g (sat 2g)	**Cholesterol** 68mg
Protein 19g	**Sodium** 518mg
Carbohydrate 11g	

Exchanges: 2 vegetable, 2 lean meat

Sweet Potato Shepherd's Pie

3 medium russet potatoes (about 1 pound total), peeled and cubed
2 medium sweet potatoes (about 1 pound total), peeled and cubed
1/4 cup fat-free (skim) milk
1/4 teaspoon salt
Nonstick cooking spray
1 pound 93% lean ground turkey
2 packages (4 ounces each) sliced mixed mushrooms *or* 8 ounces sliced cremini mushrooms
1 jar (12 ounces) fat-free beef gravy
1/2 teaspoon dried thyme
1/4 teaspoon black pepper
3/4 cup frozen baby peas, thawed

1. Place russet and sweet potato cubes in medium saucepan. Cover with water; bring to a boil. Reduce heat; simmer, covered, 20 minutes or until potatoes are very tender. Drain potatoes; return to saucepan. Mash potatoes; stir in milk and salt.

2. Meanwhile, preheat broiler. Spray large ovenproof skillet with cooking spray. Crumble turkey into skillet; add mushrooms. Cook and stir over medium-high heat until turkey is no longer pink and mushrooms begin to give off their liquid; drain. Add gravy, thyme and pepper; simmer 5 minutes. Stir in peas; cook until heated through. Remove skillet from heat.

3. Spread potato mixture over turkey mixture; spray with cooking spray. Broil 4 to 5 inches from heat source about 5 minutes or until mixture is hot and topping begins to brown.

Makes 4 servings

Nutrients per Serving: 1 wedge (1/4 of total recipe)

Calories 389	**Fiber** 7g
Fat 7g (sat 2g)	**Cholesterol** 65mg
Protein 32g	**Sodium** 740mg
Carbohydrate 51g	

Exchanges: 3 starch, 1 vegetable, 3 lean meat

Pork and Potato Packets

`low sodium` `high fiber`

- 2 packages (12 ounces each) fresh mixed vegetable medley
- 4 slices pork tenderloin (about 1/4 pound each), trimmed and pounded to 1/2-inch thickness
- 2 cups shredded hash brown potatoes
- 4 tablespoons low-sodium barbecue sauce
- 8 tablespoons water

1. Preheat oven to 550°F. Cut 4 pieces (16 inches long) nonstick foil. (Or, use regular foil lightly coated with nonstick cooking spray.)

2. Place vegetables in large bowl. Pick out carrots and place in even layer on foil pieces.

3. Place 1 tenderloin slice on top of carrots on each piece of foil. Top evenly with remaining vegetable mixture, 1/2 cup potatoes, 1 tablespoon barbecue sauce and 2 tablespoons water.

4. Double fold sides and ends of foil to seal packets, leaving head space for heat circulation. Place packets on baking sheet. Bake 25 minutes or until pork is no longer pink in center.

5. To serve, open foil packets carefully. Slide contents onto plates. *Makes 4 servings*

Nutrients per Serving: 1 packet

Calories 278	**Fiber** 6g
Fat 7g (sat 2g)	**Cholesterol** 54mg
Protein 21g	**Sodium** 130mg
Carbohydrate 29g	

Exchanges: 2 starch, 2-1/2 lean meat

Tip

Be sure to pound all of the pork pieces to an even thickness so they will cook evenly. You can pound the pork with a meat mallet or rolling pin, or flatten it with the heel of your hand or the flat side of a large knife.

Sausage and White Beans

`high fiber`

Quick Recipe

- Nonstick cooking spray
- 6 ounces turkey breakfast sausage
- 6 ounces sliced mushrooms
- 3/4 cup chopped onion
- 1/2 large red bell pepper, chopped
- 1/2 teaspoon Italian seasoning
- 1/8 teaspoon red pepper flakes (optional)
- 3/4 cup canned white beans, rinsed and drained
- 1/4 cup water
- 2 tablespoons chopped fresh parsley
- 1/2 teaspoon salt
- 1 cup quick-cooking brown rice, cooked according to package directions without salt and fat

1. Spray large nonstick skillet with cooking spray; heat over medium-high heat. Cook sausage until no longer pink, stirring to separate meat. Remove from skillet; set aside.

2. Add mushrooms, onion, bell pepper, Italian seasoning and red pepper flakes, if desired, to same skillet. Spray vegetables with cooking spray and cook, stirring frequently, 4 minutes or just until edges begin to brown.

3. Stir in beans, water and reserved sausage. Cook 1 minute or until heated through. Remove from heat and stir in parsley and salt. Serve over rice. *Makes 4 servings*

Nutrients per Serving: 3/4 cup sausage and vegetable mixture and 1/2 cup rice

Calories 286	**Fiber** 5g
Fat 9g (sat 3g)	**Cholesterol** 30mg
Protein 15g	**Sodium** 577mg
Carbohydrate 39g	

Exchanges: 2 starch, 1 vegetable, 2 lean meat

Creamy Curry Lemon Chicken

(Pictured below)

- 1/2 cup fat-free sour cream
- 1/4 cup reduced-fat mayonnaise
- 2 tablespoons lemon juice
- 1 teaspoon curry powder
- 1/2 teaspoon sugar
- 1/2 teaspoon salt
- 1/2 teaspoon black pepper
- 4 boneless skinless chicken breasts (about 1/4 pound each)
- 1 cup fresh whole wheat bread crumbs (about 2 slices bread)

1. Preheat oven to 400°F. Combine sour cream, mayonnaise, lemon juice, curry powder, sugar, salt and pepper in small bowl until blended.

2. Coat small baking pan with nonstick cooking spray. Arrange chicken pieces in pan; spread sour cream mixture evenly over chicken. Sprinkle with bread crumbs. Bake 30 to 40 minutes or until chicken is no longer pink in center. *Makes 4 servings*

Serving Suggestion: Serve with rice pilaf and steamed snow peas.

Nutrients per Serving: 1 chicken breast

Calories 254	**Fiber** 1g
Fat 7g (sat 2g)	**Cholesterol** 71mg
Protein 29g	**Sodium** 560mg
Carbohydrate 17g	

Exchanges: 1 starch, 3 lean meat

Creamy Curry Lemon Chicken

Sides & Salads

ঙ ঙ ঙ

Sesame-Honey Vegetable Casserole

Quick Recipe   *(Pictured at left)*

1 package (16 ounces) frozen mixed vegetable medley, such as baby carrots, broccoli, onions and red bell peppers, thawed and drained

3 tablespoons honey

1 tablespoon dark sesame oil

1 tablespoon reduced-sodium soy sauce

2 teaspoons sesame seeds

1. Preheat oven to 350°F. Spray 1-1/2-quart shallow casserole with nonstick cooking spray. Place vegetables in prepared dish.

2. Combine honey, sesame oil, soy sauce and sesame seeds in small bowl; stir until well blended. Drizzle evenly over vegetables. Bake 20 to 25 minutes or until vegetables are tender, stirring after 15 minutes.   *Makes 4 servings*

Nutrients per Serving: 3/4 cup vegetables

Calories 177	**Fiber** 3g
Fat 5g (sat 1g)	**Cholesterol** 0mg
Protein 4g	**Sodium** 96mg
Carbohydrate 28g	

Exchanges: 2 vegetable, 1 starch, 1 fat

Clockwise from top left: *Zesty Pasta Salad (page 106), Festive Corn Casserole (page 108), Sesame-Honey Vegetable Casserole and Double-Baked Potato (page 108)*

105

Apple Slaw with Poppy Seed Dressing

Quick Recipe (Pictured at right)

- **1 cup coarsely chopped unpeeled Jonathan apple**
- **1 teaspoon lemon juice**
- **2 tablespoons fat-free sour cream**
- **1 tablespoon plus 1-1/2 teaspoons fat-free (skim) milk**
- **1 tablespoon frozen apple juice concentrate, thawed**
- **1 teaspoon sugar**
- **3/4 teaspoon poppy seeds**
- **1/2 cup sliced carrots**
- **1/3 cup shredded green cabbage**
- **1/3 cup shredded red cabbage**
- **2 tablespoons finely chopped green bell pepper**
- **Additional cabbage leaves (optional)**

1. Combine apple and lemon juice in resealable food storage bag. Seal bag; toss to coat.

2. Combine sour cream, milk, apple juice concentrate, sugar and poppy seeds in small bowl; stir until well blended. Add apple mixture, carrots, cabbage and bell pepper; toss to coat. Serve on cabbage leaves, if desired.

Makes 2 servings

Nutrients per Serving: 1-1/4 cups apple slaw with dressing

Calories 100	**Fiber** 3g
Fat 1g (sat <1g)	**Cholesterol** <1mg
Protein 2g	**Sodium** 39mg
Carbohydrate 22g	

Exchanges: 1 fruit, 1 vegetable

Zesty Pasta Salad

Quick Recipe (Pictured on page 104)

- **2 cups (about 4 ounces) uncooked tricolor rotini pasta**
- **1 cup sliced fresh mushrooms**
- **3/4 cup canned diced tomatoes**
- **1/2 cup sliced green bell pepper**
- **1/4 cup chopped onion**
- **1/4 cup fat-free Italian salad dressing**
- **2 tablespoons freshly grated Parmesan cheese**
- **Fresh lettuce leaves (optional)**

1. Cook pasta according to package directions, omitting salt. Rinse with cool water; drain.

2. Combine pasta, mushrooms, tomatoes, bell pepper and onion in large bowl. Pour salad dressing over pasta mixture; toss to coat.

3. Top with cheese just before serving. Garnish with fresh lettuce leaves, if desired.

Makes 6 servings

Nutrients per Serving: about 3/4 cup pasta salad

Calories 96	**Fiber** 1g
Fat 1g (sat <1g)	**Cholesterol** 2mg
Protein 4g	**Sodium** 222mg
Carbohydrate 17g	

Exchanges: 1 starch, 1/2 vegetable

Tip

Tricolor pasta gets its color from vegetables. Beets and tomatoes make it red, carrots make it orange and spinach makes it green.

Apple Slaw with Poppy Seed Dressing

Double-Baked Potatoes

(Pictured on page 104)

3 large baking potatoes
1/4 cup fat-free (skim) milk, warmed
1 cup (4 ounces) shredded reduced-fat
   cheddar cheese
3/4 cup frozen corn, thawed and drained
1 tablespoon finely chopped fresh
   oregano *or* 1 teaspoon dried oregano
1/2 teaspoon chili powder
   Nonstick cooking spray
1 cup chopped onion
1/2 to 1 cup chopped poblano chili
   peppers*
3 cloves garlic, minced
1/2 teaspoon salt
1/4 teaspoon black pepper
3 tablespoons chopped fresh cilantro

*Chili peppers can sting and irritate the skin, so wear rubber gloves when handling peppers and do not touch your eyes.

1. Preheat oven to 400°F. Scrub potatoes with soft vegetable brush under running water; rinse. Pierce potatoes with fork. Wrap each potato in foil. Bake about 1 hour or until fork-tender. Remove potatoes; set aside until cool enough to handle. *Reduce oven temperature to 350°F.*

2. Cut potatoes in half lengthwise; scoop out insides, being careful not to tear shells. Set shells aside. Beat potato insides in large bowl with electric mixer at medium speed until coarsely mashed. Add milk; beat until smooth. Stir in cheese, corn, oregano and chili powder. Set aside.

3. Spray medium skillet with cooking spray. Add onion, poblano peppers and garlic; cook and stir 5 to 8 minutes or until tender. Stir in salt and black pepper.

4. Spoon potato mixture into reserved potato shells. Top with onion mixture. Place stuffed potato halves in baking pan. Bake 20 to 30 minutes or until heated through. Sprinkle with cilantro.   *Makes 6 servings*

Nutrients per Serving: 1 stuffed potato half

Calories 176	**Fiber** 1g
Fat 3g (sat 1g)	**Cholesterol** 10mg
Protein 7g	**Sodium** 451mg
Carbohydrate 31g	

Exchanges: 2 starch, 1/2 lean meat, 1/2 fat

ઌ ઌ ઌ

Festive Corn Casserole

(Pictured on page 104)

2 cups grated zucchini
1 cup frozen corn
1 cup diced red bell pepper
2 cups cholesterol-free egg substitute
1/2 cup evaporated skimmed milk
2 teaspoons sugar substitute*
1/4 teaspoon celery seed
1/8 teaspoon salt
1/8 teaspoon red pepper flakes (optional)

*This recipe was tested with sucralose-based sugar substitute.

1. Preheat oven to 350°F. Spray 11×7-inch baking dish with nonstick cooking spray.

2. Combine zucchini, corn and bell pepper in baking dish. Whisk egg substitute, evaporated milk, sugar substitute, celery seed, salt and red pepper flakes, if desired, in large bowl; pour over vegetables in baking dish. Bake 45 to 55 minutes or until set and golden.
           Makes 10 servings

Nutrients per Serving: about 1/2 cup casserole

Calories 54	**Fiber** 1g
Fat <1g (sat 0g)	**Cholesterol** <1mg
Protein 6g	**Sodium** 138mg
Carbohydrate 7g	

Exchanges: 1 vegetable, 1 lean meat

Fruit Salad with Cherry Vinaigrette

Quick Recipe (Pictured at bottom right)

Cherry Vinaigrette

> 1/2 cup fresh sweet cherries, pitted and chopped
> 1/4 cup orange juice
> 2 tablespoons balsamic vinegar
> 1 to 2 tablespoons honey
> 1 tablespoon canola oil
> 1/8 teaspoon salt (optional)

Fruit Salad

> 3 cups cantaloupe cubes
> 1 large mango, peeled and diced
> 1/4 cup sliced almonds

1. For vinaigrette, combine cherries, orange juice, vinegar, honey, oil and salt, if desired, in small bowl; stir until well blended. Let stand 5 minutes for flavors to blend.

2. For fruit salad, combine cantaloupe and mango in large bowl. Add dressing just before serving; stir well. Sprinkle with almonds.

Makes 8 servings

Variation: If fresh cherries aren't available, use frozen cherries, thawed and well-drained.

Nutrients per Serving: 1/2 cup fruit salad with vinaigrette

Calories 75	**Fiber** 1g
Fat 2g (sat <1g)	**Cholesterol** 0mg
Protein <1g	**Sodium** 11mg
Carbohydrate 15g	

Exchanges: 1 fruit

Lemon Brussels Sprouts

Quick Recipe

> 2-1/2 cups frozen brussels sprouts
> 1 tablespoon water
> 1/2 teaspoon lemon juice
> 1/4 teaspoon grated lemon peel
> Dash black pepper (optional)
> Dash ground thyme (optional)

Microwave Directions

1. Combine brussels sprouts, water, lemon juice and lemon peel in 1-quart microwavable casserole; cover. Microwave on HIGH 3 minutes.

2. Stir to break apart; cover. Microwave on HIGH 2 to 3 minutes or until brussels sprouts are tender. Drain; sprinkle with pepper and thyme, if desired. *Makes 4 servings*

Note: This recipe was tested in an 1100-watt microwave oven.

Nutrients per Serving: 1/2 cup brussels sprouts

Calories 30	**Fiber** 2g
Fat <1g (sat <1g)	**Cholesterol** 0mg
Protein 3g	**Sodium** 16mg
Carbohydrate 6g	

Exchanges: 1 vegetable

Fruit Salad with Cherry Vinaigrette

Buttermilk Mashed Potatoes

Buttermilk Mashed Potatoes

(Pictured above)

2 pounds medium red boiling potatoes, peeled and cut into chunks
4 cloves garlic, peeled
3/4 cup low-fat buttermilk
1/2 teaspoon salt
1/4 teaspoon black pepper
2 tablespoons snipped fresh chives (optional)

1. Place potatoes and garlic in large saucepan. Add enough water to cover; bring to a boil over high heat. Reduce heat; simmer, uncovered, 20 to 30 minutes or until potatoes are fork-tender. Drain.

2. Place potatoes and garlic in medium bowl. Mash with potato masher or beat with electric mixer at medium speed until smooth.

3. Add buttermilk, salt and pepper; stir just until blended. Sprinkle with chives, if desired.

Makes 8 servings

Nutrients per Serving: 1/2 cup mashed potatoes

Calories 101	**Fiber** 2g
Fat <1g (sat <1g)	**Cholesterol** 1mg
Protein 3g	**Sodium** 175mg
Carbohydrate 22g	

Exchanges: 1-1/2 starch

Peperonata

Quick Recipe

1 tablespoon extra-virgin olive oil
4 large red, yellow or orange bell peppers, cut into thin strips
2 cloves garlic, coarsely chopped
12 pimiento-stuffed green olives or pitted black olives, halved
2 to 3 tablespoons white wine vinegar or red wine vinegar
1/4 teaspoon salt
1/4 teaspoon black pepper

1. Heat olive oil in 12-inch skillet over medium-high heat. Add bell peppers; cook, stirring frequently, 8 to 9 minutes or until edges begin to brown.

2. Reduce heat to medium. Add garlic; cook and stir 1 to 2 minutes. *Do not allow garlic to brown.* Add olives, vinegar, salt and black pepper. Cook 1 to 2 minutes or until all liquid has evaporated.

Makes 4 servings

Nutrients per Serving: about 2/3 cup peperonata

Calories 89	**Fiber** 3g
Fat 5g (sat 1g)	**Cholesterol** 0mg
Protein 1g	**Sodium** 309mg
Carbohydrate 8g	

Exchanges: 1 vegetable, 1 fat

Tip

Traditionally, peperonata is served hot as a condiment or side dish with meat dishes. It goes great with chicken and pork. Or, it can be chilled and served as part of an appetizer selection.

Artichoke Wild Rice Salad

 low sodium · meatless

(Pictured at bottom right)

1 jar (about 6 ounces) marinated artichoke hearts, undrained
2 cups cooked wild rice
1 cup frozen peas, thawed
1 can (8 ounces) sliced water chestnuts, drained
1 cup (4 ounces) shredded mozzarella cheese (optional)
1 jar (2 ounces) diced pimiento, drained
2 tablespoons canola oil
1 tablespoon balsamic vinegar
1/2 teaspoon dried tarragon
1/2 teaspoon Dijon mustard
2 to 3 drops hot pepper sauce

1. Drain artichokes, reserving 2 tablespoons liquid.

2. Combine artichokes, rice, peas, water chestnuts, cheese and pimiento in large bowl. Combine oil, reserved liquid from artichokes, vinegar, tarragon, mustard and hot pepper sauce in small bowl; pour over rice mixture and toss. Refrigerate 4 hours or overnight to allow flavors to blend. Serve cold. *Makes 6 to 8 servings*

Variation: Combine wild rice with white or brown rice. Cook the rices separately, since they have different cooking times, then combine them after they are cooked.

Favorite recipe from **Minnesota Cultivated Wild Rice Council**

Nutrients per Serving: about 3/4 cup salad (without cheese)

Calories 129	**Fiber** 3g
Fat 4g (sat <1g)	**Cholesterol** 0mg
Protein 4g	**Sodium** 48mg
Carbohydrate 22g	

Exchanges: 1 starch, 1 vegetable, 1/2 fat

Salmon Pasta Salad

 cooking for 1 or 2

Quick Recipe

1 cup cooked medium pasta shells, drained and cooled
1 can (6 ounces) salmon, drained
1/2 cup finely chopped celery
2 tablespoons finely chopped red bell pepper
2 tablespoons chopped fresh parsley
2 tablespoons fat-free mayonnaise
1 green onion, finely chopped
1 tablespoon lemon juice
2 teaspoons capers
1/8 teaspoon paprika

Combine all ingredients in medium bowl. Serve immediately or refrigerate, covered, up to 2 hours before serving. *Makes 2 servings*

Nutrients per Serving: 1-1/2 cups salad

Calories 262	**Fiber** 2g
Fat 9g (sat 2g)	**Cholesterol** 21mg
Protein 18g	**Sodium** 627mg
Carbohydrate 26g	

Exchanges: 1-1/2 starch, 1 vegetable, 2 lean meat, 1/2 fat

Artichoke Wild Rice Salad

Green Bean Casserole

(Pictured at right)

Nonstick cooking spray
Ranch-Style White Sauce (recipe follows)
1 cup chopped onion
2 cloves garlic, minced
1-1/2 cups sliced mushrooms
1-1/4 pounds fresh green beans, cooked until crisp-tender
1 cup fresh bread crumbs (2 slices bread)
2 tablespoons minced fresh parsley

1. Preheat oven to 350°F. Spray 1-1/2-quart casserole with cooking spray. Prepare Ranch-Style White Sauce; set aside. Spray medium skillet with cooking spray; heat over medium-high heat. Add onion and garlic; cook 2 to 3 minutes or until tender. Remove half of onion mixture; set aside.

2. Add mushrooms to skillet; cook about 5 minutes or until tender. Combine mushroom mixture, beans and white sauce in prepared casserole.

3. Spray medium skillet with cooking spray; heat over medium heat. Add bread crumbs; spray top of crumbs lightly with cooking spray. Cook and stir 3 to 4 minutes or until crumbs are golden. Stir in reserved onion mixture and parsley. Sprinkle bread crumb mixture over casserole. Bake, uncovered, 20 to 30 minutes or until heated through.   *Makes 6 servings*

Ranch-Style White Sauce

1-1/2 tablespoons butter
3 tablespoons all-purpose flour
1-1/2 cups fat-free (skim) milk
3 to 4 teaspoons dry ranch-style salad dressing mix
1/4 to 1/2 teaspoon white pepper

Melt butter in small saucepan over low heat. Stir in flour; cook 1 to 2 minutes, stirring constantly.

Stir in milk using wire whisk; bring to a boil. Cook, whisking constantly, 1 to 2 minutes or until thickened. Stir in dressing mix and pepper.
Makes 1-1/2 cups

Nutrients per Serving: 2/3 cup casserole

Calories 123	**Fiber** 1g
Fat 3g (sat 1g)	**Cholesterol** 1mg
Protein 5g	**Sodium** 200mg
Carbohydrate 19g	

Exchanges: 1 starch, 1-1/2 vegetable, 1/2 fat

ॐ ॐ ॐ

Spiced Honey Carrots

Quick Recipe

1 package (16 ounces) peeled baby carrots
1-1/4 cups boiling water
1/8 teaspoon ground cloves
1/8 teaspoon ground cinnamon
1-1/2 tablespoons honey
1 tablespoon 50% less fat margarine
Grated peel and juice of 1/2 SUNKIST® lemon

In covered saucepan, cook carrots in gently boiling water with cloves and cinnamon until just tender, about 8 to 10 minutes; drain well. Add honey, margarine, lemon peel and lemon juice; heat through.   *Makes 4 servings*

Nutrients per Serving: 2/3 cup carrots

Calories 83	**Fiber** 2g
Fat 2g (sat <1g)	**Cholesterol** 0mg
Protein 1g	**Sodium** 74mg
Carbohydrate 17g	

Exchanges: 2 vegetable, 1/2 starch, 1/2 fat

Green Bean Casserole

Tabbouleh

1/2 cup uncooked bulgur wheat
3/4 cup boiling water
1/4 teaspoon salt
    5 teaspoons lemon juice
    2 teaspoons olive oil
1/2 teaspoon dried basil
1/4 teaspoon black pepper
    1 green onion, thinly sliced
1/2 cup chopped cucumber
1/2 cup chopped green bell pepper
1/2 cup chopped tomato
1/4 cup chopped fresh parsley
    2 teaspoons chopped fresh mint

1. Rinse bulgur thoroughly in colander under cold water; drain well. Transfer to medium heatproof bowl. Stir in boiling water and salt. Cover; let stand 30 minutes. Drain well.

2. Combine lemon juice, oil, basil and black pepper in small bowl. Pour over cooked bulgur; mix well.

3. Layer bulgur, green onion, cucumber, bell pepper and tomato in bowl; sprinkle with parsley and mint.

4. Refrigerate, covered, at least 2 hours to allow flavors to blend. Serve layered, or toss before serving. *Makes 6 servings*

Nutrients per Serving: about 1/3 cup tabbouleh

Calories 65	**Fiber** 4g
Fat 1g (sat <1g)	**Cholesterol** 0mg
Protein 1g	**Sodium** 95mg
Carbohydrate 12g	

Exchanges: 1/2 starch, 1 vegetable

Tart & Tangy Cherry Salad

    1 cup diet lemon-lime soda
    1 package (0.3 ounce) sugar-free cherry gelatin
    1 can (14-1/2 ounces) pitted tart red cherries in water
    1 can (11 ounces) mandarin orange segments
1/4 cup sugar substitute*
    1 container (8 ounces) fat-free whipped topping
1/4 cup finely chopped walnuts

*This recipe was tested with sucralose-based sugar substitute.

1. Heat soda in small microwavable bowl on HIGH 1 minute.

2. Transfer soda to large bowl. Whisk in gelatin until completely dissolved. Drain juice from cherries and oranges into gelatin mixture. Stir until well mixed.

3. Mash cherries with potato masher or fork. Sprinkle sugar substitute over cherries; stir until well mixed.

4. Whisk cherry mixture, whipped topping and walnuts into gelatin until well blended. Fold in oranges. Pour mixture into medium bowl. Refrigerate at least 2 hours or until firm. *Makes 10 servings*

Tip: This recipe is perfect to make the day before and refrigerate overnight.

Nutrients per Serving: 1/2 cup gelatin salad

Calories 96	**Fiber** 1g
Fat 2g (sat <1g)	**Cholesterol** 0mg
Protein 1g	**Sodium** 48mg
Carbohydrate 17g	

Exchanges: 1 fruit, 1/2 fat

White Bean Salad with Cilantro Vinaigrette

(Pictured below)

1/2 cup fat-free Italian salad dressing
2 tablespoons white wine vinegar
1 tablespoon chopped fresh cilantro *or*
   1 teaspoon dried cilantro
2 teaspoons sugar
2 teaspoons olive oil
1 medium red bell pepper
6 green onions
2 cans (about 15 ounces each) great
   northern beans, rinsed and drained
Purple kale leaves (optional)
Fresh cilantro leaves (optional)

1. Combine dressing, vinegar, cilantro, sugar and oil in small bowl; set aside.

2. Cut bell pepper into 1/4-inch strips. Cut green onions into 1/4-inch slices. Combine with beans in medium bowl.

3. Pour reserved dressing mixture over salad; stir gently until salad is evenly coated with dressing. Cover; refrigerate 2 hours or overnight.

4. Garnish with purple kale and fresh cilantro, if desired. *Makes 8 servings*

Nutrients per Serving: 1/2 cup salad

Calories 122	**Fiber** 7g
Fat 2g (sat <1g)	**Cholesterol** <1mg
Protein 6g	**Sodium** 508mg
Carbohydrate 19g	

Exchanges: 1 starch, 1/2 vegetable, 1/2 lean meat

White Bean Salad with Cilantro Vinaigrette

Vegetables with Spinach Fettuccine

Vegetables with Spinach Fettuccine

low fat · low sodium · meatless

(Pictured above)

1 cup water
6 sun-dried tomatoes (not packed in oil)
3 ounces uncooked spinach fettuccine
1 tablespoon olive oil
1/4 cup chopped onion
1/4 cup sliced red bell pepper
1 clove garlic, minced
1/2 cup sliced mushrooms
1/2 cup packed coarsely chopped stemmed spinach
1/4 teaspoon salt
1/4 teaspoon ground nutmeg
1/8 teaspoon black pepper

1. Bring water to a boil in small saucepan. Pour over sun-dried tomatoes in small heatproof bowl. Let stand 30 minutes. Drain tomatoes; cut into strips.

2. Meanwhile, cook pasta according to package directions, omitting salt. Drain.

3. Heat oil in large nonstick skillet over medium heat until hot. Add onion, bell pepper and garlic; cook and stir 3 minutes or until

vegetables are crisp-tender. Add mushrooms and spinach; cook and stir 1 minute. Add sun-dried tomatoes, pasta, salt, nutmeg and black pepper; cook and stir 1 to 2 minutes or until heated through.   *Makes 6 servings*

Nutrients per Serving: 1/2 cup fettuccine

Calories 82	**Fiber** 1g
Fat 3g (sat <1g)	**Cholesterol** 3mg
Protein 3g	**Sodium** 101mg
Carbohydrate 13g	

Exchanges: 1/2 starch, 1 vegetable, 1/2 fat

Plum Ratatouille

low fat · low sodium · meatless

2-1/2 cups diced eggplant
2 cups sliced zucchini
1 onion, cut into wedges
1 tablespoon vegetable oil
2 cups diced tomatoes
2 cups fresh California plum wedges
2 teaspoons minced garlic
1-1/2 teaspoons dried basil leaves, crushed
1 teaspoon dried oregano leaves, crushed
1/4 teaspoon pepper
Fresh lemon juice

In large nonstick skillet, cook and stir eggplant, zucchini and onion in oil 15 minutes or until tender. Add remaining ingredients except lemon juice; reduce heat and cover. Cook, stirring occasionally, until plums are tender, about 4 minutes. Drizzle with fresh lemon juice just before serving.   *Makes 6 servings*

Favorite recipe from **California Tree Fruit Agreement**

Nutrients per Serving: 1 cup ratatouille

Calories 69	**Fiber** 3g
Fat 3g (sat <1g)	**Cholesterol** 0mg
Protein 1g	**Sodium** 4mg
Carbohydrate 12g	

Exchanges: 1/2 fruit, 1 vegetable, 1/2 fat

Asparagus Spears with Sun-Dried Tomatoes

low fat | low sodium | low carb

1-1/2 cups water, divided
1/2 cup sun-dried tomatoes (not packed in oil)
1 clove garlic, minced
2 tablespoons balsamic vinegar
1 teaspoon sugar
1/4 teaspoon dried oregano
1/4 teaspoon dried basil
1/8 teaspoon black pepper
1/2 cup water
16 asparagus spears (about 1 pound), trimmed

1. Bring 1 cup water to a boil in small saucepan. Pour over sun-dried tomatoes in small heatproof bowl. Let stand 30 minutes; drain and coarsely chop. Process tomatoes and garlic in food processor or blender until smooth. Add vinegar, sugar, oregano, basil and pepper. Blend well; set aside.

2. Bring remaining 1/2 cup water to a boil in large skillet over high heat. Add asparagus; return to a boil. Reduce heat to medium-low. Simmer, covered, about 5 minutes or until asparagus is crisp-tender. Drain. Serve hot or cold with tomato mixture.   *Makes 4 servings*

Nutrients per Serving: 4 asparagus spears with 2 tablespoons tomato mixture

Calories 49	**Fiber** 1g
Fat 1g (sat <1g)	**Cholesterol** 0mg
Protein 3g	**Sodium** 20mg
Carbohydrate 8g	

Exchanges: 2 vegetable

Tip

Trim dried, shriveled or woody stems from asparagus spears before cooking. If the stem ends are still too thick or woody, peel them with a paring knife or vegetable peeler so that they will cook as quickly as the tender tips.

Italian-Style Collard Greens

low fat | high fiber | meatless

Quick Recipe

1/2 pound collard greens
1 teaspoon olive oil
1 cup coarsely chopped celery
3/4 cup coarsely chopped onion
2 cloves garlic, minced
1 can (14-1/2 ounces) no-salt-added stewed tomatoes, undrained
2 teaspoons Italian seasoning
1 can (about 15 ounces) white beans (such as cannellini, great northern or navy), rinsed and drained

1. Remove discolored leaves and tough stems from greens. Wash greens thoroughly in cold water to remove any sand; drain and pat dry. Coarsely chop.

2. Heat oil in large saucepan over medium heat. Add celery, onion and garlic; cook and stir 5 minutes. Add chopped greens, stewed tomatoes with juice and seasoning. Cook and stir, breaking up tomatoes, until greens wilt.

3. Bring to a boil over high heat. Reduce heat to low. Simmer, covered, 15 minutes.

4. Add beans; simmer, covered, 5 minutes or until heated through.   *Makes 4 servings*

Nutrients per Serving: 1-1/4 cups greens

Calories 148	**Fiber** 10g
Fat 2g (sat <1g)	**Cholesterol** 0mg
Protein 10g	**Sodium** 233mg
Carbohydrate 32g	

Exchanges: 1 starch, 2-1/2 vegetable, 1/2 fat

Cranberry Salad

(Pictured at right)

2 cups cranberries

1 cup water

1 cup EQUAL® SPOONFUL*

1 small package cranberry or cherry sugar-free gelatin

1 cup boiling water

1 cup diced celery

1 can (7-1/4 ounces) crushed pineapple, in juice

1/2 cup chopped walnuts

*May substitute 24 packets EQUAL® sweetener.

• Bring cranberries and 1 cup water to a boil. Remove from heat when cranberries have popped open. Add Equal® and stir. Set aside to cool.

• Dissolve gelatin with 1 cup boiling water. Add cranberry sauce; mix thoroughly. Add celery, pineapple and walnuts. Pour into mold or bowl. Place in refrigerator until set.

Makes 8 servings

Nutrients per Serving: about 1/2 cup gelatin salad

Calories 96	**Fiber** 2g
Fat 5g (sat <1g)	**Cholesterol** 0mg
Protein 2g	**Sodium** 49mg
Carbohydrate 12g	

Exchanges: 1 fruit, 1 fat

Tip

If fresh cranberries aren't available in the produce section of the grocery store, try looking for frozen cranberries in the freezer section. It's a good idea to buy a few extra bags when fresh are available and store them in the freezer so that you'll have them when you need them.

Turkey Fruited Bow Tie Salad

Quick Recipe

1/2 pound cooked turkey breast, cut into 1/2-inch cubes

2 cups bow tie pasta, cooked according to package directions and drained

1 can (10-1/2 ounces) mandarin oranges, drained

1 medium red apple, chopped

1 cup seedless grapes, cut in half

1/2 cup celery, sliced

1/2 cup low-fat lemon yogurt

2 tablespoons frozen orange juice concentrate, thawed

1/4 teaspoon ground ginger

1. In large bowl, combine turkey, pasta, oranges, apple, grapes and celery.

2. In small bowl, combine yogurt, juice and ginger. Fold dressing into turkey mixture and toss to coat. Cover and refrigerate until ready to serve.

Makes 4 servings

Favorite recipe from **National Turkey Federation**

Nutrients per Serving: 2 cups salad

Calories 269	**Fiber** 3g
Fat 2g (sat 1g)	**Cholesterol** 49mg
Protein 22g	**Sodium** 71mg
Carbohydrate 43g	

Exchanges: 2 starch, 1/2 fruit, 2 lean meat

Cranberry Salad

Warm Blackened Tuna Salad

Warm Blackened Tuna Salad

(Pictured above)

> 5 cups torn romaine lettuce
>
> 2 cups coarsely shredded red cabbage
>
> 2 medium yellow or green bell peppers, cut into strips
>
> 1-1/2 cups sliced zucchini
>
> 1 teaspoon onion powder
>
> 1/2 teaspoon garlic powder
>
> 1/2 teaspoon black pepper
>
> 1/2 teaspoon ground red pepper
>
> 1/2 teaspoon dried thyme
>
> 3/4 pound fresh or thawed frozen tuna steaks, cut 1 inch thick
>
> 1/3 cup water
>
> 3/4 cup onion slices
>
> 2 tablespoons balsamic vinegar
>
> 1-1/2 teaspoons Dijon mustard
>
> 1 teaspoon canola oil
>
> 1/2 teaspoon chicken bouillon granules

1. Spray broiler pan with nonstick cooking spray. Preheat broiler. Combine lettuce, cabbage, bell peppers and zucchini in large bowl; set aside.

2. Combine onion powder, garlic powder, black pepper, ground red pepper and thyme in small bowl. Rub spice mixture onto both sides of tuna. Place tuna on broiler pan. Broil 4 inches from heat about 10 minutes or until fish flakes when tested with a fork, turning halfway through broiling time. Set aside and keep warm.

3. For dressing, bring water to a boil in small saucepan over high heat. Add onion; reduce heat to medium-low. Simmer, covered, 4 to 5 minutes or until onion is tender. Add vinegar, mustard, oil and bouillon granules; cook and stir until heated through.

4. Divide romaine mixture evenly among 4 salad plates; slice tuna and arrange on top. Drizzle with dressing. Serve warm.

Makes 4 servings

Nutrients per Serving: 2-3/4 cups salad

Calories 196	**Fiber** 4g
Fat 6g (sat 1g)	**Cholesterol** 32mg
Protein 23g	**Sodium** 185mg
Carbohydrate 13g	

Exchanges: 2-1/2 vegetable, 2-1/2 lean meat

ಶಿ ಶಿ ಶಿ

Vegetable Fried Rice

Quick Recipe

> 1 teaspoon canola oil
>
> 1-1/2 cups small broccoli florets
>
> 1/2 cup chopped red bell pepper
>
> 2 cups chilled cooked white rice
>
> 1 tablespoon reduced-sodium soy sauce
>
> 1/2 cup shredded carrot

1. Heat oil in large nonstick skillet over medium heat. Add broccoli and bell pepper; stir-fry 3 minutes or until crisp-tender.

2. Add rice and soy sauce; stir-fry 2 minutes. Add carrot; heat through.   *Makes 4 servings*

Nutrients per Serving: 1 cup fried rice

Calories 193	**Fiber** 5g
Fat 2g (sat <1g)	**Cholesterol** 0mg
Protein 5g	**Sodium** 278mg
Carbohydrate 40g	

Exchanges: 2 starch, 2 vegetable

Healthy Chopped Salad

low fat · low carb

Quick Recipe   (Pictured at bottom right)

- 2 romaine lettuce hearts
- 2 cups baby spinach
- 1 tomato
- 1 cup baby carrots
- 1 package (8 ounces) ready-to-use sugar snap peas
- 3 cups chopped cooked skinless turkey breast
- 2 cups chopped bok choy (about 1 small head)
- Juice of 1 lemon
- Juice of 1 lime
- 1 tablespoon smooth peanut butter
- 2 teaspoons sugar substitute*
- 2 teaspoons sesame seeds
- 1 teaspoon chopped garlic
- 1/2 teaspoon black pepper (optional)

This recipe was tested with sucralose-based sugar substitute.

1. Chop romaine, spinach, tomato, carrots and snap peas. Combine in large bowl. Add turkey and bok choy. Set aside.

2. Combine lemon juice, lime juice, peanut butter, sugar substitute, sesame seeds, garlic and black pepper, if desired, in 1-pint jar with tight-fitting lid. Shake well.

3. Pour dressing over salad; toss well.

Makes 8 servings

Nutrients per Serving: about 2 cups salad

Calories 96	**Fiber** 2g
Fat 2g (sat <1g)	**Cholesterol** 29mg
Protein 13g	**Sodium** 174mg
Carbohydrate 7g	

Exchanges: 2 vegetable, 1 lean meat

Broiled Zucchini Halves

low carb · meatless

Quick Recipe

- 1/2 cup (2 ounces) shredded mozzarella cheese
- 2 tablespoons diced pimiento
- 2 tablespoons chopped black olives
- 4 small zucchini (about 1/4 pound each), sliced lengthwise
- 1 tablespoon olive oil

1. Preheat broiler. Combine cheese, pimiento and olives in small bowl; set aside.

2. Brush zucchini halves with oil; arrange on foil-lined broiler pan. Broil 6 inches from heat 5 minutes or until fork-tender. Spoon 2 tablespoons cheese mixture onto each zucchini half. Broil until cheese melts and browns. Serve immediately.

Makes 4 servings

Nutrients per Serving: 2 zucchini halves

Calories 94	**Fiber** 1g
Fat 7g (sat 2g)	**Cholesterol** 8mg
Protein 5g	**Sodium** 144mg
Carbohydrate 5g	

Exchanges: 1 vegetable, 1-1/2 fat

Healthy Chopped Salad

Pasta with Onions and Goat Cheese

(Pictured at right)

        2 teaspoons olive oil
        4 cups thinly sliced sweet onions
    3/4 cup (3 ounces) crumbled goat cheese
    1/4 cup fat-free (skim) milk
        6 ounces (2-1/4 cups) uncooked bowtie
            or other small pasta
        1 clove garlic, minced
        2 tablespoons fat-free reduced-sodium
            chicken broth or dry white wine
    1-1/2 teaspoons chopped fresh sage *or*
        1/2 teaspoon dried sage
    1/2 teaspoon salt
    1/4 teaspoon black pepper
        2 tablespoons chopped toasted walnuts

1. Heat oil in large nonstick skillet over medium heat. Add onions; cook slowly, stirring occasionally, about 20 to 25 minutes or until golden and caramelized.

2. Meanwhile, combine goat cheese and milk in small bowl until well blended. Set aside.

3. Cook pasta according to package directions, omitting salt; drain. Set aside.

4. Add garlic to onions in skillet; cook about 3 minutes or until softened. Add chicken broth, sage, salt and pepper; cook until liquid has evaporated. Remove from heat. Add pasta and goat cheese mixture; stir until cheese is melted. Sprinkle with walnuts.   *Makes 8 servings*

Nutrients per Serving: 1/2 cup pasta mixture

Calories 150	**Fiber** 2g
Fat 5g (sat <1g)	**Cholesterol** 9mg
Protein 5g	**Sodium** 107mg
Carbohydrate 21g	

Exchanges: 1 starch, 1 vegetable, 1 fat

Vegetable Risotto

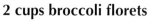
meatless

        2 cups broccoli florets
        1 cup finely chopped zucchini
        1 cup finely chopped yellow squash
        1 cup finely chopped red bell pepper
    2-1/2 cups fat-free reduced-sodium vegetable
            broth
        1 tablespoon olive oil
        2 tablespoons finely chopped onion
    1/2 cup uncooked arborio or other
            short-grain rice
    1/4 cup dry white wine or water
    1/3 cup freshly grated Parmesan cheese

1. Steam broccoli, zucchini, yellow squash and bell pepper 3 minutes or just until crisp-tender. Rinse with cold water; drain. Set aside.

2. Bring broth to a simmer in small saucepan; keep hot on low heat.

3. Heat oil in large heavy saucepan over medium-high heat. Add onion. Reduce heat to medium. Cook and stir about 5 minutes or until onion is translucent. Add rice, stirring to coat with oil. Add wine; cook and stir until almost dry. Add 1/2 cup hot broth; cook and stir until broth is absorbed. Continue adding broth, 1/2 cup at a time, allowing broth to absorb before each addition and stirring frequently. (Total cooking time is about 20 minutes.)

4. Remove from heat; stir in cheese. Add steamed vegetables; mix well. Serve immediately.   *Makes 6 servings*

Nutrients per Serving: 2/3 cup risotto

Calories 123	**Fiber** 2g
Fat 4g (sat 1g)	**Cholesterol** 4mg
Protein 5g	**Sodium** 240mg
Carbohydrate 19g	

Exchanges: 1 starch, 1 vegetable, 1/2 lean meat

*Pasta with Onions and
Goat Cheese*

Broccoli with Red Pepper and Shallots

Marinated Black-Eyed Pea and Tomato Salad

high fiber | meatless

2 tablespoons cider vinegar
1 tablespoon extra-virgin olive oil
1/2 teaspoon dried thyme
1/4 teaspoon salt
1/4 teaspoon hot pepper sauce
1 can (about 15 ounces) black-eyed peas, rinsed and drained
1 cup diced fresh tomatoes
1/2 cup finely chopped Anaheim or green bell pepper
1/2 cup chopped fresh parsley
1/4 cup finely chopped red onion

1. Whisk together vinegar, olive oil, thyme, salt and hot pepper sauce in small bowl.

2. Combine peas, tomatoes, Anaheim pepper, parsley and red onion in serving bowl. Pour vinaigrette over all; gently stir to coat.

3. Cover and refrigerate at least 1 hour.
Makes 4 servings

Nutrients per Serving: 1 cup salad

Calories 145	**Fiber** 5g
Fat 4g (sat 1g)	**Cholesterol** 0mg
Protein 6g	**Sodium** 478mg
Carbohydrate 22g	

Exchanges: 1 starch, 1 vegetable, 1 fat

ॐ ॐ ॐ

Broccoli with Red Pepper and Shallots

low fat | meatless

Quick Recipe   *(Pictured at left)*

2-1/4 pounds broccoli
2 quarts water
2 teaspoons butter
1 large red bell pepper, cut into short thin strips
3 large shallots *or* 1 small onion, thinly sliced
1/2 teaspoon salt
1/4 teaspoon black pepper
1/4 cup sliced almonds, toasted* (optional)

*Spread nuts in shallow baking pan. Bake in preheated 350°F oven 5 to 10 minutes or until fragrant, stirring occasionally.

1. Cut broccoli into florets. Peel stems and cut into 1-inch pieces. Bring water to a boil in large saucepan over high heat. Add broccoli; boil, uncovered, 3 to 5 minutes or until bright green and tender. Drain and rinse under cold water; drain well.

2. Melt butter in 12-inch nonstick skillet over medium heat. Add bell pepper and shallots; cook 3 minutes, stirring occasionally. Add broccoli; cook 4 to 6 minutes, stirring occasionally. Sprinkle with salt and black pepper; mix well. Garnish with almonds, if desired. *Makes 6 servings*

Nutrients per Serving: 1-1/3 cups broccoli mixture

Calories 65	**Fiber** 4g
Fat 2g (sat <1g)	**Cholesterol** 0mg
Protein 5g	**Sodium** 248mg
Carbohydrate 11g	

Exchanges: 2 vegetable

Lemon Tossed Linguine

Quick Recipe

8 ounces uncooked linguine
3 tablespoons fresh lemon juice
2 teaspoons reduced-fat margarine
2 tablespoons minced chives
1/3 cup fat-free (skim) milk
1 teaspoon cornstarch
1 tablespoon minced fresh dill *or*
    1 teaspoon dried dill weed
1 tablespoon minced fresh parsley *or*
    1 teaspoon dried parsley flakes
2 teaspoons grated lemon peel
1/4 teaspoon white pepper
3 tablespoons grated Romano or
    Parmesan cheese

1. Cook pasta according to package directions, omitting salt; drain well. Place in medium bowl; sprinkle lemon juice over pasta.

2. Meanwhile, melt margarine in small saucepan over medium heat. Add chives; cook until chives are soft. Combine milk and cornstarch in small bowl; stir into saucepan. Cook and stir until thickened. Stir in dill, parsley, lemon peel and pepper.

3. Pour sauce over pasta. Sprinkle with cheese; toss to coat evenly. Serve immediately.

Makes 8 servings

Nutrients per Serving: 1/2 cup linguine

Calories 173	**Fiber** 2g
Fat 3g (sat 1g)	**Cholesterol** 7mg
Protein 8g	**Sodium** 110mg
Carbohydrate 27g	

Exchanges: 1-1/2 starch, 1/2 lean meat, 1/2 fat

Gourmet Deli Potato & Pea Salad

1-1/2 pounds new potatoes, scrubbed and
    quartered
1 cup water
3/4 teaspoon salt, divided
1/2 pound sugar snap peas or snow peas,
    trimmed
1/3 cup reduced-fat mayonnaise
1/3 cup plain nonfat yogurt
3 tablespoons *French's®* Honey Dijon
    Mustard
1/3 cup finely chopped red onion
2 tablespoons minced fresh dill *or*
    2 teaspoons dried dill weed
1 clove garlic, minced

Microwave Directions

1. Place potatoes, water and 1/2 teaspoon salt in 3-quart microwave-safe baking dish. Cover and microwave on HIGH 15 minutes or until potatoes are tender, stirring once. Add peas. Cover and microwave on HIGH 3 minutes or until peas are crisp-tender. Rinse with cold water and drain. Cool completely.

2. Combine mayonnaise, yogurt, mustard, onion, dill, garlic and remaining 1/4 teaspoon salt in large bowl; mix well. Add potatoes and peas; toss to coat evenly. Cover and refrigerate 1 hour before serving. Garnish as desired.

Makes 6 servings

Note: This recipe was tested in an 1100-watt microwave oven.

Nutrients per Serving: 1 cup salad

Calories 179	**Fiber** 3g
Fat 5g (sat 1g)	**Cholesterol** <1mg
Protein 4g	**Sodium** 448mg
Carbohydrate 29g	

Exchanges: 2 starch, 1 fat

Soups & Sandwiches

ɞ ɞ ɞ

Pizza Turnovers

Quick Recipe   *(Pictured at left)*

> **5 ounces mild Italian bulk turkey sausage**
> **1/2 cup pizza sauce**
> **1 package (13.8 ounces) refrigerated pizza dough**
> **1/3 cup shredded reduced-fat Italian cheese blend**

1. Preheat oven to 425°F. Brown sausage in nonstick saucepan over medium heat, stirring to separate meat. Drain fat. Add pizza sauce; cook and stir until hot.

2. Spray baking sheet with nonstick cooking spray. Unroll pizza dough onto baking sheet. Pat into 12×8-inch rectangle. Cut into 6 (4×4-inch) squares. Divide sausage mixture evenly among squares. Sprinkle with cheese. Lift one corner of each square and fold over filling to opposite corner, making triangle. Press edges with tines of fork to seal.

3. Bake 11 to 13 minutes or until golden brown.

Makes 6 servings

Nutrients per Serving: 1 turnover

Calories 188	**Fiber** 3g
Fat 6g (sat 2g)	**Cholesterol** 17mg
Protein 10g	**Sodium** 502mg
Carbohydrate 24g	

Exchanges: 1-1/2 starch, 1/2 lean meat, 1/2 fat

***Clockwise from top left:** 5-Minute Soup (page 134), Pizza Turnovers, Summer Minestrone (page 139) and Open-Faced Chicken Sandwich with Roasted Pepper Mayo (page 132)*

Chicken & Orzo Soup

Quick Recipe   *(Pictured at right)*

Nonstick cooking spray

3 ounces boneless skinless chicken breast, cut into bite-size pieces

1 can (about 14 ounces) fat-free reduced-sodium chicken broth

1 cup water

2/3 cup shredded carrot

1/3 cup sliced green onions

1/4 cup (about 2 ounces) uncooked orzo pasta

1 teaspoon grated fresh ginger

1/8 teaspoon ground turmeric

2 teaspoons lemon juice

1/8 teaspoon black pepper (optional)

Sliced green onions (optional)

1. Spray medium saucepan with cooking spray; heat over medium-high heat. Add chicken; cook and stir 2 to 3 minutes or until cooked through. Remove from saucepan; set aside.

2. In same saucepan, combine broth, water, carrot, green onions, orzo, ginger and turmeric; bring to a boil. Reduce heat; simmer, covered, 8 to 10 minutes or until orzo is tender. Stir in chicken and lemon juice; cook until hot. Season with pepper, if desired.

3. Ladle into serving bowls. Sprinkle with additional green onions, if desired.

Makes 2 servings

Nutrients per Serving: 1-1/2 cups soup

Calories 152	**Fiber** 2g
Fat 1g (sat <1g)	**Cholesterol** 25mg
Protein 14g	**Sodium** 492mg
Carbohydrate 21g	

Exchanges: 1 starch, 1 vegetable, 1-1/2 lean meat

California Salmon Burger

Quick Recipe

1-1/3 pounds boneless, skinless salmon, cut into chunks

1 cup Sliced California Ripe Olives, divided

1/4 cup chopped fresh chives

2 teaspoons crushed fennel seeds

1 teaspoon minced lemon zest

3/4 teaspoon kosher salt

6 whole-grain hamburger buns

1/4 cup thinly sliced shallots

3 cups loosely packed arugula leaves

2 tablespoons lemon juice

1. Place salmon in bowl of food processor and pulse 3 to 5 times until coarsely ground. Transfer to clean mixing bowl and stir in 3/4 cup California Ripe Olives, chives, fennel seeds, lemon zest and salt.

2. Form into 6 patties and grill over medium-high heat for 4 to 6 minutes on each side. While burgers are cooking, slice buns in half and place on grill until lightly toasted, then transfer to serving plates.

3. Combine shallots, arugula, lemon juice and remaining California Ripe Olives in small mixing bowl. Set aside.

4. Place 1 cooked burger on the bottom half of each bun. Top with arugula mixture and remaining buns.   *Makes 6 servings*

Favorite recipe from **California Olive Industry**

Nutrients per Serving: 1 sandwich

Calories 330	**Fiber** 3g
Fat 15g (sat 4g)	**Cholesterol** 50mg
Protein 25g	**Sodium** 685mg
Carbohydrate 23g	

Exchanges: 1-1/2 starch, 3 lean meat, 1 fat

Chicken & Orzo Soup

Turkey Taco Burger Wraps

high fiber

Quick Recipe

6 (7- to 8-inch) whole wheat or spinach tortillas
1 can (4 ounces) diced mild green chiles, drained
1/2 cup uncooked quick oats
1/4 cup sliced green onions
1 egg, beaten
1 teaspoon dried oregano
1 teaspoon ground cumin
1/4 teaspoon salt
1/4 teaspoon black pepper
1 pound 93% lean ground turkey or 95% lean ground beef
1-1/2 cups shredded romaine lettuce
1/4 cup taco sauce

1. Preheat oven to 350°F. Wrap tortillas in foil. Bake 10 minutes. Remove from oven. *Do not open foil.*

2. Combine chiles, oats, green onions, egg, oregano, cumin, salt and pepper in large bowl. Add ground turkey; mix well. Shape into 6 (4×2-inch) oval patties.

3. Spray rack of broiler pan with nonstick cooking spray. Place patties on rack. Broil 3 to 4 inches from heat source 10 to 12 minutes or until no longer pink in center (165°F), turning once.

4. To serve, place each patty on one warm tortilla. Top with lettuce and taco sauce. Wrap tortillas around patties. *Makes 6 servings*

Nutrients per Serving: 1 wrap

Calories 284	**Fiber** 5g
Fat 10g (sat 2g)	**Cholesterol** 82mg
Protein 22g	**Sodium** 610mg
Carbohydrate 26g	

Exchanges: 2 starch, 2 lean meat, 1/2 fat

Sausage, Squash & Kale Stew

high fiber

Quick Recipe

3 cups cubed peeled butternut squash (1/2-inch cubes)
1/2 cup plus 1 tablespoon water, divided
3/4 pound hot or mild Italian turkey sausage
1 can (14-1/2 ounces) no-salt-added whole tomatoes, chopped
6 cups coarsely chopped stemmed fresh kale or Swiss chard (about 1 pound)
1/4 teaspoon black pepper
1/4 cup grated Parmesan or Romano cheese

1. Place squash in medium microwavable bowl. Add 1 tablespoon water. Cover; microwave on HIGH 4 to 6 minutes or just until tender.

2. Meanwhile, remove sausage from casings; crumble into large saucepan. Brown sausage over medium heat, stirring to separate meat. Drain fat. Stir in tomatoes with juice and remaining 1/2 cup water. Top with kale. Cover; cook over medium-low heat 7 to 8 minutes. Stir in squash and pepper. Cover; cook 5 minutes. Ladle into bowls; top with cheese.

Makes 4 servings

Nutrients per Serving: 1-1/2 cups stew

Calories 276	**Fiber** 5g
Fat 10g (sat 3g)	**Cholesterol** 47mg
Protein 21g	**Sodium** 802mg
Carbohydrate 32g	

Exchanges: 1-1/2 starch, 2 vegetable, 2 lean meat, 1/2 fat

Tip

Kale, a nutrient-rich member of the cabbage family, is available year-round; it is best, however, in the winter months. Choose deep-colored kale in small bunches with firm leaves; avoid bunches with limp or discolored leaves. Store kale in a plastic bag in the refrigerator up to 2 days.

Antipasto Italian Roll-Ups

Quick Recipe   *(Pictured below)*

- **1 tablespoon fat-free sour cream**
- **1 tablespoon sun-dried tomato pesto**
- **2 (6-inch) whole wheat tortillas**
- **1/2 cup fresh basil leaves**
- **1/3 cup chopped jarred roasted red peppers**
- **2 ounces part-skim mozzarella cheese, thinly sliced**
- **2 thin slices turkey salami (about 1/2 ounce each)**

1. Combine sour cream and sun-dried tomato pesto in small bowl.

2. Spread 1 tablespoon tomato mixture down center of each tortilla. Divide remaining ingredients evenly between tortillas; roll up.

Makes 2 servings

Nutrients per Serving: 1 roll-up

Calories 251	**Fiber** 3g
Fat 11g (sat 4g)	**Cholesterol** 36mg
Protein 14g	**Sodium** 715mg
Carbohydrate 24g	

Exchanges: 1 starch, 1 vegetable, 2 lean meat, 1 fat

Antipasto Italian Roll-Ups

Tuscan Vegetable Stew

high fiber · meatless

Quick Recipe　　(Pictured at right)

2 tablespoons olive oil

2 teaspoons minced garlic

2 packages (4 ounces each) sliced mixed exotic mushrooms *or* 1 package (8 ounces) sliced button mushrooms

1/4 cup sliced shallots or chopped sweet onion

1 can (14-1/2 ounces) Italian-style stewed tomatoes, undrained and chopped

1 jar (7 ounces) roasted red peppers, drained and cut into 1-inch pieces (optional)

1 can (about 15 ounces) cannellini beans, rinsed and drained

2 tablespoons chopped fresh basil *or* 2 teaspoons dried basil

1 tablespoon balsamic vinegar

Salt and black pepper (optional)

Grated Romano, Parmesan or Asiago cheese (optional)

1. Heat oil and garlic in large deep skillet over medium heat. Add mushrooms and shallots; cook and stir 5 minutes.

2. Add tomatoes with juice, peppers and beans to skillet; bring to a boil. Reduce heat to medium-low. Cover; simmer 10 minutes, stirring once.

3. Stir basil and vinegar into stew; add salt and black pepper to taste, if desired. Sprinkle each serving with cheese, if desired.

Makes 4 servings

Nutrients per Serving: 1 cup stew

Calories 212	**Fiber** 7g
Fat 7g (sat 1g)	**Cholesterol** 0mg
Protein 8g	**Sodium** 408mg
Carbohydrate 30g	

Exchanges: 1 starch, 2-1/2 vegetable, 1-1/2 fat

Open-Faced Chicken Sandwiches with Roasted Pepper Mayo

high fiber

Quick Recipe　　(Pictured on page 126)

4 boneless skinless chicken breasts (about 1/4 pound each)

1 teaspoon dried thyme

1 teaspoon garlic salt

1/4 teaspoon black pepper

1 teaspoon olive oil or butter

1/4 cup reduced-fat mayonnaise

1 jar (2 ounces) diced pimiento, drained, *or* 3 tablespoons chopped jarred roasted red pepper

4 slices multi-grain, rye or sourdough bread, lightly toasted

1 cup packed watercress leaves or baby spinach leaves

1. Place chicken between 2 sheets of waxed paper or plastic wrap; pound to 1/3-inch thickness. Sprinkle thyme, garlic salt and pepper over chicken.

2. Heat oil in large nonstick skillet over medium heat. Add chicken; cook 4 to 5 minutes per side or until no longer pink in center.

3. Meanwhile, combine mayonnaise and pimiento; mix well. Spread each toast slice with about 1-1/2 teaspoons mayonnaise mixture. Place 1/4 cup watercress on each slice of toast; top each with 1 chicken breast and another 1-1/2 teaspoons mayonnaise mixture.

Makes 4 servings

Nutrients per Serving: 1 sandwich

Calories 245	**Fiber** 5g
Fat 8g (sat 1g)	**Cholesterol** 71mg
Protein 30g	**Sodium** 470mg
Carbohydrate 16g	

Exchanges: 1 starch, 1/2 vegetable, 3-1/2 lean meat

Tuscan Vegetable Stew

5-Minute Soup

Quick Recipe   *(Pictured on page 126)*

> 1 can (about 15 ounces) navy beans, rinsed and drained
> 1 can (14-1/2 ounces) Italian-style stewed tomatoes
> 1 cup water
> 1-1/2 teaspoons dried basil
> 1/2 teaspoon sugar
> 1/2 teaspoon chicken bouillon granules
> 2 teaspoons olive oil

1. Combine all ingredients except oil in medium saucepan.

2. Bring to a boil over high heat. Reduce heat; simmer 5 minutes, uncovered. Remove from heat; stir in oil.   *Makes 4 servings*

Nutrients per Serving: about 3/4 cup soup

Calories 175	**Fiber** 7g
Fat 3g (sat <1g)	**Cholesterol** <1mg
Protein 9g	**Sodium** 742mg
Carbohydrate 29g	

Exchanges: 1-1/2 starch, 1-1/2 vegetable, 1/2 lean meat

Tip

This soup is perfect for lunch on the run. Make it in the morning, put it in a vacuum flask and take it with you.

BBQ Pork Sandwiches with Slaw

> 1 pork tenderloin (about 1 pound)
> 1/4 teaspoon plus 1/8 teaspoon salt, divided
> 1/4 teaspoon black pepper
> 6 tablespoons hickory smoked barbecue sauce, divided
> 1-1/2 cups thinly sliced green cabbage or cabbage slaw mix
> 1 medium Granny Smith apple, peeled and coarsely grated
> 1/4 cup sliced green onions
> 1 tablespoon reduced-fat mayonnaise
> 1/2 teaspoon apple cider vinegar
> 4 whole wheat sandwich buns, toasted

1. Preheat oven to 400°F.

2. Place pork in roasting pan. Sprinkle with 1/4 teaspoon salt and pepper. Brush with 2 tablespoons barbecue sauce. Bake 25 to 30 minutes, turning once during baking. Let stand 5 minutes; cut into 16 (1/4-inch) slices.

3. Meanwhile, combine cabbage, apple, green onions, mayonnaise, vinegar and remaining 1/8 teaspoon salt in medium bowl; mix well.

4. Place remaining 4 tablespoons barbecue sauce in small microwavable bowl; cover and microwave on HIGH 30 seconds or until sauce is heated.

5. To serve, place 4 slices of pork on each bun. Spread 1 tablespoon barbecue sauce over pork on each sandwich. Top each sandwich with 1/3 cup slaw. Serve immediately.
                      Makes 4 servings

Nutrients per Serving: 1 sandwich

Calories 338	**Fiber** 6g
Fat 6g (sat 1g)	**Cholesterol** 74mg
Protein 28g	**Sodium** 731mg
Carbohydrate 43g	

Exchanges: 3 starch, 3 lean meat

Clam Chowder

Quick Recipe *(Pictured at bottom right)*

1 can (6-1/2 ounces) whole baby clams, undrained
1 potato, peeled and coarsely chopped
1/4 cup finely chopped onion
2/3 cup evaporated skimmed milk
1/8 teaspoon white pepper
1/8 teaspoon dried thyme
1 tablespoon butter
Red pepper strips (optional)
Fresh thyme sprigs (optional)
Fresh greens (optional)

1. Drain clams; reserve juice. Add enough water to reserved juice to measure 2/3 cup. Combine clam juice mixture, potato and onion in large saucepan. Bring to a boil over high heat. Reduce heat to medium-low. Simmer, covered, 8 minutes or until potato is tender.

2. Add milk, pepper and thyme to saucepan. Increase heat to medium-high. Cook and stir 2 minutes. Add butter. Cook 5 minutes or until soup thickens slightly, stirring occasionally.

3. Stir in clams. Cook 5 minutes or until heated through, stirring occasionally. Garnish with red pepper strips, thyme and greens, if desired.

Makes 2 servings

Nutrients per Serving: 1-1/2 cups chowder

Calories 298	**Fiber** 2g
Fat 9g (sat 5g)	**Cholesterol** 92mg
Protein 24g	**Sodium** 627mg
Carbohydrate 34g	

Exchanges: 1 starch, 1 milk, 1 vegetable, 1-1/2 lean meat, 1/2 fat

Vegetable Pitas

Quick Recipe

1 (6-inch) whole wheat pita bread round
2 Boston or red leaf lettuce leaves
1-1/2 cups chopped assorted vegetables (broccoli florets, julienned carrots, red and yellow bell peppers, sliced mushrooms)
2 tablespoons crumbled reduced-fat feta cheese
1-1/2 tablespoons reduced-fat balsamic or raspberry vinaigrette dressing

Cut pita round in half crosswise. Open pockets. Line with lettuce leaves. Combine vegetables, cheese and dressing in small bowl; mix well. Spoon into pita halves.

Makes 1 serving

Nutrients per Serving: 2 pita halves

Calories 238	**Fiber** 6g
Fat 5g (sat 2g)	**Cholesterol** 5mg
Protein 11g	**Sodium** 885mg
Carbohydrate 43g	

Exchanges: 2-1/2 starch, 2 vegetable, 1/2 lean meat

Clam Chowder

Lima Bean and Escarole Soup

`low fat` `low sodium` `high fiber`

(Pictured at right)

1-1/2 cups dried baby lima beans, sorted and rinsed
1 teaspoon olive oil
1/2 cup chopped celery
1/3 cup coarsely chopped onion
2 cloves garlic, minced
2 cans (14-1/2 ounces each) no-salt-added whole tomatoes, undrained, chopped
1/2 cup chopped fresh parsley
2 tablespoons chopped fresh rosemary
1/4 teaspoon black pepper
3 cups shredded escarole or spinach

1. Place dried lima beans in large glass bowl; cover completely with water. Soak 6 to 8 hours or overnight. Drain beans; place in large saucepan or Dutch oven. Cover beans with about 3 cups water. Bring to a boil over high heat; reduce heat to low. Cover; simmer about 1 hour or until soft. Drain.

2. Heat oil in small skillet over medium heat. Add celery, onion and garlic; cook and stir 5 minutes or until onion is tender. Remove from heat.

3. Add celery mixture and tomatoes with juice to beans. Stir in parsley, rosemary and pepper. Cover; simmer over low heat 15 minutes. Add escarole; simmer 5 minutes.

Makes 6 servings

Nutrients per Serving: 1-1/2 cups soup

Calories 196	**Fiber** 5g
Fat 2g (sat 0g)	**Cholesterol** 0mg
Protein 12g	**Sodium** 33mg
Carbohydrate 35g	

Exchanges: 2 starch, 2 vegetable

Open-Faced Smoked Turkey and Asparagus Sandwiches

`high fiber`

Quick Recipe

1 box (10 ounces) BIRDS EYE® frozen Deluxe Asparagus Cuts
1/2 pound smoked turkey breast, cubed
2 tablespoons creamy mustard blend
1 teaspoon honey
4 thick slices whole grain bread, lightly toasted
Lettuce leaves
1 large tomato, sliced

• In small saucepan, cook asparagus according to package directions; drain in colander and rinse under cold water to cool.

• In large bowl, combine asparagus, turkey, mustard and honey.

• To assemble sandwiches, line bread slices with lettuce. Top with tomato and turkey mixture, dividing evenly. *Makes 4 servings*

Nutrients per Serving: 1 open-faced sandwich (made with 1/2 cup turkey mixture)

Calories 161	**Fiber** 5g
Fat 4g (sat 1g)	**Cholesterol** 15mg
Protein 18g	**Sodium** 810mg
Carbohydrate 26g	

Exchanges: 1 starch, 2 vegetable, 2 lean meat

Lima Bean and Escarole Soup

Wild Rice Soup

Wild Rice Soup

 low fat | high fiber | meatless

(Pictured above)

1/2 cup dried lentils

1 package (6 ounces) long grain and wild rice mix

1 can (about 14 ounces) vegetable broth

1 package (10 ounces) frozen mixed vegetables

1 cup fat-free (skim) milk

2 slices (1 ounce each) reduced-fat American cheese, cut into pieces

1. Rinse and sort lentils. Place lentils in small saucepan; cover with about 3 cups water. Bring to a boil; reduce heat to low. Simmer, covered, 5 minutes. Let stand, covered, 1 hour. Drain and rinse lentils.

2. Cook rice mix according to package directions in medium saucepan. Add lentils and remaining ingredients. Bring to a boil; reduce heat to low. Simmer, uncovered, 20 minutes.

Makes 6 servings

Nutrients per Serving: 1 cup soup

Calories 231	**Fiber** 7g
Fat 3g (sat 1g)	**Cholesterol** 6mg
Protein 13g	**Sodium** 585mg
Carbohydrate 41g	

Exchanges: 3 starch, 1/2 fat

Caribbean Jerk Chicken Open-Faced Sandwiches

Quick Recipe

4 boneless skinless chicken breasts (about 1/4 pound each)

2 small yellow or red bell peppers, seeded and quartered

1/3 cup hickory-flavored barbecue sauce

2 teaspoons Caribbean jerk seasoning

4 tablespoons reduced-fat mayonnaise

4 slices whole wheat or whole grain bread, lightly toasted

1 cup packed arugula leaves or spinach leaves

1. Prepare grill for direct grilling. Place chicken and bell peppers on grid over medium coals.

2. Combine barbecue sauce and jerk seasoning; set aside.

3. Grill, covered, 5 minutes. Turn; brush sauce mixture over chicken and bell peppers. Grill 4 to 6 minutes or until chicken is no longer pink in center and peppers are tender.

4. Spread 1 tablespoon mayonnaise onto each piece of toast; top with arugula, peppers and chicken.

Makes 4 servings

Nutrients per Serving: 1 sandwich

Calories 251	**Fiber** 3g
Fat 7g (sat 2g)	**Cholesterol** 43mg
Protein 21g	**Sodium** 709mg
Carbohydrate 26g	

Exchanges: 1 starch, 1 vegetable, 3 lean meat

Tip

Use long-handled tongs to turn the chicken instead of using a grill fork. When the chicken is pierced, juices escape. Also, watch the chicken and peppers carefully during grilling. The total cooking time will vary with their position on the grill, the weather and the temperature of the coals.

Summer Minestrone

low fat | high fiber | meatless

(Pictured on page 126)

Olive oil cooking spray
2 carrots, sliced
1 cup halved green beans
1/2 cup sliced celery
1/2 cup thinly sliced leek
2 cloves garlic, minced
1 tablespoon fresh sage *or* 1 teaspoon dried sage
1 tablespoon fresh oregano *or* 1 teaspoon dried oregano
3 cans (about 14 ounces each) vegetable broth
1 medium zucchini, halved lengthwise and cut into 1/2-inch-thick slices
1 cup quartered mushrooms
8 ounces cherry tomatoes, halved
1/4 cup minced fresh parsley
3 ounces (3/4 cup) uncooked rotini pasta
Salt and black pepper (optional)
8 teaspoons grated Parmesan cheese

1. Spray large saucepan with cooking spray. Heat over medium heat. Add carrots, green beans, celery, leek, garlic, sage and oregano; cook and stir 3 to 5 minutes. Add vegetable broth; bring to a boil. Reduce heat. Simmer about 5 minutes or until vegetables are just crisp-tender.

2. Add zucchini, mushrooms, tomatoes and parsley; bring to a boil. Stir in pasta. Reduce heat; simmer, uncovered, about 8 minutes or until pasta and vegetables are tender. Season to taste with salt and pepper, if desired. Ladle soup into bowls; sprinkle each with 1 teaspoon Parmesan cheese.   *Makes 8 servings*

Nutrients per Serving: 1 cup minestrone

Calories 167	**Fiber** 6g
Fat 1g (sat <1g)	**Cholesterol** 1mg
Protein 9g	**Sodium** 293mg
Carbohydrate 31g	

Exchanges: 1-1/2 starch, 1-1/2 vegetable, 1/2 lean meat

Ham and Spinach Calzones

8 cups torn fresh spinach leaves
8 cups boiling water
1 loaf (16 ounces) frozen whole wheat bread dough, thawed
1 cup reduced-fat ricotta cheese
2 teaspoons Italian seasoning
1-1/2 teaspoons minced garlic
4 ounces lean ham, finely chopped
3 ounces reduced-fat Swiss cheese, thinly sliced
2/3 cup reduced-fat reduced-sodium garlic and herb pasta sauce, heated

1. Preheat oven to 375°F. Spray baking sheet with nonstick cooking spray; set aside.

2. Place spinach in large colander set in sink. Slowly pour boiling water over spinach until wilted. Drain well, pressing out excess moisture.

3. Divide dough into 6 equal portions. Roll each portion into 6-inch circle on lightly floured surface.

4. Combine ricotta cheese, Italian seasoning and garlic in small bowl; mix well. Spread over half of each dough circle, leaving 1/2-inch border at edge. Top with spinach, ham and Swiss cheese. Moisten edges of dough circles with water. Fold dough over filling; crimp edges with fork to seal. Prick tops.

5. Place on prepared baking sheet. Bake about 20 minutes or until golden brown. Serve warm with pasta sauce.   *Makes 6 servings*

Nutrients per Serving: 1 calzone with 5 teaspoons pasta sauce

Calories 330	**Fiber** 4g
Fat 9g (sat 3g)	**Cholesterol** 27mg
Protein 22g	**Sodium** 758mg
Carbohydrate 43g	

Exchanges: 2-1/2 starch, 1 vegetable, 2 lean meat, 1/2 fat

Buttons & Bows

Quick Recipe   *(Pictured at right)*

   1 teaspoon olive oil
 1/3 cup minced onion
 1/3 cup sliced carrot
   3 cups sliced fresh mixed mushrooms
   1 teaspoon ground sage
 1/4 teaspoon ground thyme
 1/4 teaspoon black pepper
 1/4 cup dry red wine
   2 cans (about 14 ounces each) reduced-
      fat reduced-sodium beef broth
 1/4 cup tomato paste
   2 ounces (1/2 cup) uncooked small bow
      tie pasta

1. Heat oil in large saucepan over medium heat until hot. Add onion and carrot; cook 2 minutes. Add mushrooms, sage, thyme and pepper; cook and stir 5 minutes or until mushrooms are tender.

2. Add wine; cook 2 minutes or until wine is reduced by half. Add beef broth; bring to a boil over medium-high heat.

3. Stir in tomato paste and pasta. Cover; cook, stirring occasionally, 10 to 12 minutes or until pasta is tender.

4. Ladle soup into individual bowls. Serve immediately.   *Makes 4 servings*

Nutrients per Serving: 3/4 cup soup

Calories 129	**Fiber** 2g
Fat 2g (sat <1g)	**Cholesterol** 0mg
Protein 7g	**Sodium** 512mg
Carbohydrate 18g	

Exchanges: 1 starch, 1 vegetable, 1/2 fat

Cucumber Cheese Melts

Quick Recipe

   1 ounce fat-free cream cheese, softened
   1 tablespoon crumbled blue cheese
   4 slices multi-grain bread
   2 tablespoons sugar-free apricot fruit
      spread
   8 cucumber slices
   1 ounce shaved deli ham
   2 slices (1 ounce each) fat-free Swiss
      cheese
   Butter-flavored cooking spray

1. Mix cream cheese and blue cheese in small bowl; spread on 2 bread slices. Spread apricot fruit spread over cheese. Top with cucumber slices, ham, Swiss cheese and remaining bread slices.

2. Lightly spray large skillet with cooking spray. Heat over medium heat. Cook sandwiches 4 minutes or until browned on bottom. Spray tops of sandwiches with cooking spray. Turn and cook 4 minutes or until browned on other side.
        Makes 2 servings

Nutrients per Serving: 1 sandwich

Calories 246	**Fiber** 8g
Fat 5g (sat 1g)	**Cholesterol** 12mg
Protein 17g	**Sodium** 743mg
Carbohydrate 40g	

Exchanges: 2 starch, 1/2 fruit, 2 lean meat

Travelin' Turkey Subs

3 tablespoons plain low-fat yogurt

3 tablespoons reduced-fat ranch salad dressing

1-1/2 cups finely chopped cooked boneless skinless turkey breast or smoked turkey breast

1/2 cup finely chopped broccoli

1/3 cup shredded carrot

4 whole wheat or multi-grain hot dog or hamburger buns, split

1/2 cup (2 ounces) shredded reduced-fat cheddar cheese

2 tablespoons sunflower seeds or chopped toasted* slivered almonds (optional)

Spread nuts in shallow baking pan. Bake in preheated 350°F oven 5 to 10 minutes or until fragrant, stirring occasionally.

1. Combine yogurt and salad dressing in medium bowl. Add turkey, broccoli and carrot; mix well.

2. Slightly hollow out tops and bottoms of buns. Sprinkle 2 tablespoons cheese on each bun bottom. Top each with 1/2 cup turkey mixture. Sprinkle with seeds, if desired. Top with bun tops, cut side down.

3. Wrap subs in plastic wrap. Refrigerate 2 hours or until thoroughly chilled.

Makes 4 servings

Nutrients per Serving: 1 sandwich

Calories 275	**Fiber** 6g
Fat 7g (sat 2g)	**Cholesterol** 48mg
Protein 21g	**Sodium** 379mg
Carbohydrate 35g	

Exchanges: 2 starch, 2-1/2 lean meat

Dijon Lamb Stew

Quick Recipe

1/2 pound boneless lamb, cut into small pieces*

1/2 medium onion, chopped

1/2 teaspoon dried rosemary

1 tablespoon olive oil

1 can (14-1/2 ounces) DEL MONTE® Stewed Tomatoes - Seasoned with Basil, Garlic & Oregano

1 carrot, julienne cut

1 tablespoon Dijon mustard

1 can (15 ounces) white beans or pinto beans, drained

Top sirloin steak can be substituted for lamb.

1. Brown meat with onion and rosemary in oil in large skillet over medium-high heat, stirring occasionally. Season with salt and pepper, if desired.

2. Add undrained tomatoes, carrot and mustard. Cover and cook over medium heat 10 minutes; add beans.

3. Cook, uncovered, over medium heat 5 minutes, stirring occasionally. Garnish with sliced ripe olives and chopped parsley, if desired.

Makes 4 servings

Nutrients per Serving: about 3/4 cup stew (without salt, pepper or garnishes)

Calories 274	**Fiber** 8g
Fat 7g (sat 2g)	**Cholesterol** 37mg
Protein 20g	**Sodium** 351mg
Carbohydrate 32g	

Exchanges: 2 starch, 1 vegetable, 2 lean meat

Hearty Mushroom Barley Soup

`low fat` `high fiber`

(Pictured at bottom right)

Nonstick cooking spray
1 teaspoon olive oil
2 cups chopped onions
1 cup thinly sliced carrots
2 cans (about 14 ounces each) fat-free reduced-sodium chicken broth
12 ounces sliced fresh mushrooms
1 can (about 10-3/4 ounces) 98% fat-free reduced-sodium cream of mushroom soup, undiluted
1/2 cup uncooked quick-cooking barley
1 teaspoon Worcestershire sauce
1/2 teaspoon dried thyme
1/4 cup finely chopped green onions
1/4 teaspoon salt (optional)
1/4 teaspoon black pepper

1. Spray Dutch oven or large saucepan with cooking spray; heat over medium-high heat. Add oil; tilt pan to coat bottom. Add onions; cook and stir 8 minutes or until onions just begin to turn golden. Add carrots; cook and stir 2 minutes.

2. Add chicken broth, mushrooms, cream of mushroom soup, barley, Worcestershire sauce and thyme; bring to a boil over high heat.

3. Reduce heat; cover and simmer 15 minutes, stirring occasionally. Stir in green onions, salt and pepper. *Makes 4 servings*

Nutrients per Serving: 1-1/2 cups soup

Calories 209	**Fiber** 8g
Fat 3g (sat 1g)	**Cholesterol** 2mg
Protein 8g	**Sodium** 772mg
Carbohydrate 40g	

Exchanges: 2 starch, 2 vegetable, 1/2 fat

Curried Beef Burgers

Quick Recipe

1 pound 95% lean ground beef
1/4 cup mango chutney, chopped
1/4 cup grated apple
1-1/2 teaspoons curry powder
1/2 teaspoon salt (optional)
1/8 teaspoon black pepper
1 large red onion, sliced 1/4 inch thick
4 kaiser rolls or hamburger buns

1. Spray cold grill grid with nonstick cooking spray. Prepare grill for direct grilling.

2. Combine ground beef, chutney, apple, curry powder, salt and pepper in medium bowl; mix lightly. Shape into 4 equal-size patties.

3. Grill, covered, over medium heat 8 to 10 minutes (or uncovered 13 to 15 minutes) until no longer pink in centers, turning once. Grill onion 5 minutes or until lightly charred, turning once. Serve with burgers.

Makes 4 servings

Nutrients per Serving: 1 sandwich

Calories 365	**Fiber** 2g
Fat 8g (sat 3g)	**Cholesterol** 70mg
Protein 31g	**Sodium** 718mg
Carbohydrate 41g	

Exchanges: 3 starch, 3 lean meat

Hearty Mushroom Barley Soup

Mustard-Glazed Chicken Sandwiches

Quick Recipe   *(Pictured at right)*

1/2 cup honey-mustard barbecue sauce, divided
4 kaiser rolls, split
4 boneless skinless chicken breasts (about 1/4 pound each)
Nonstick cooking spray
4 slices (1 ounce each) reduced-fat Swiss cheese
4 leaves leaf lettuce
8 slices tomato

1. Spread about 1 teaspoon barbecue sauce onto cut sides of each roll.

2. Pound chicken breasts between 2 pieces of plastic wrap to 1/2-inch thickness with flat side of meat mallet or rolling pin. Spread remaining barbecue sauce over chicken.

3. Coat large nonstick skillet with cooking spray. Cook chicken over medium-low heat 5 minutes per side or until no longer pink in center. Remove skillet from heat. Place cheese slices on chicken; let stand 3 minutes to melt.

4. Place lettuce leaves and tomato slices on roll bottoms; top with chicken and roll tops.
Makes 4 servings

Serving Suggestion: Serve sandwiches with yellow tomatoes, baby carrots and celery sticks.

Nutrients per Serving: 1 sandwich

Calories 431	**Fiber** 2g
Fat 10g (sat 3g)	**Cholesterol** 76mg
Protein 37g	**Sodium** 702mg
Carbohydrate 46g	

Exchanges: 3 starch, 1/2 vegetable, 4 lean meat

Broccoli & Potato Chowder

Quick Recipe

1 can (about 14 ounces) fat-free reduced-sodium chicken broth
1 cup sliced leeks
1/2 cup cubed peeled potato
1/3 cup fresh or frozen corn
1 can (4 ounces) chopped mild green chiles
3/4 teaspoon paprika
1-1/2 cups broccoli florets
3/4 cup evaporated skimmed milk
2 tablespoons all-purpose flour
Jalapeño pepper sauce (optional)

1. Combine broth, leeks, potato, corn, chiles and paprika in medium saucepan. Bring to a boil. Reduce heat; simmer, covered, 10 to 15 minutes or until vegetables are tender. Add broccoli; simmer 3 minutes.

2. Whisk milk into flour. Stir into vegetable mixture. Cook, stirring constantly, until soup boils and thickens slightly. Season to taste with pepper sauce, if desired.   *Makes 2 servings*

Nutrients per Serving: 2 cups chowder

Calories 280	**Fiber** 5g
Fat 1g (sat <1g)	**Cholesterol** 3mg
Protein 19g	**Sodium** 311mg
Carbohydrate 51g	

Exchanges: 2 starch, 1/2 milk, 3 vegetable

Mustard-Glazed Chicken Sandwich

Moroccan Lentil & Vegetable Soup

(Pictured at right)

- 1 tablespoon olive oil
- 1 cup chopped onion
- 4 cloves garlic, minced
- 1/2 cup dried lentils, sorted, rinsed and drained
- 1-1/2 teaspoons ground coriander
- 1-1/2 teaspoons ground cumin
- 1/2 teaspoon black pepper
- 1/2 teaspoon ground cinnamon
- 2 cans (about 14 ounces each) vegetable broth
- 1/2 cup chopped celery
- 1/2 cup chopped sun-dried tomatoes (not packed in oil)
- 1 medium yellow summer squash, chopped
- 1/2 cup chopped green bell pepper
- 1/2 cup chopped fresh parsley
- 1 cup chopped plum tomatoes
- 1/4 cup chopped fresh cilantro or basil

1. Heat oil in medium saucepan over medium heat. Add onion and garlic; cook 4 to 5 minutes or until onion is tender, stirring occasionally. Stir in lentils, coriander, cumin, black pepper and cinnamon; cook 2 minutes. Add chicken broth, celery and sun-dried tomatoes; bring to a boil over high heat. Reduce heat to low; simmer, covered, 25 minutes.

2. Stir in squash, bell pepper and parsley. Cover; cook 10 minutes or until lentils are tender.

3. Top with plum tomatoes and cilantro just before serving. *Makes 6 servings*

Nutrients per Serving: 1-1/4 cups soup

Calories 124	**Fiber** 5g
Fat 3g (sat <1g)	**Cholesterol** 0mg
Protein 8g	**Sodium** 399mg
Carbohydrate 20g	

Exchanges: 1 starch, 1 vegetable, 1/2 lean meat

Monterey Chicken Sandwiches

Quick Recipe

- 1 tablespoon canola oil
- 1 tablespoon butter
- 4 boneless skinless chicken breasts (about 1/4 pound each)
- 1 teaspoon dried thyme
- 1/2 teaspoon salt
- 1/4 teaspoon black pepper
- 1 large red onion, thinly sliced
- 4 kaiser rolls, split
- Radicchio or lettuce leaves

1. Heat oil and butter in large skillet over medium heat. Add chicken; sprinkle with thyme. Cook 8 minutes or until browned on both sides and no longer pink in center, turning after 4 minutes. Season with salt and pepper. Remove from skillet; keep warm.

2. Add onion to skillet; cook until tender.

3. Fill rolls with radicchio leaves, chicken and onions. *Makes 4 servings*

Nutrients per Serving: 1 sandwich

Calories 366	**Fiber** 2g
Fat 10g (sat 3g)	**Cholesterol** 73mg
Protein 32g	**Sodium** 702mg
Carbohydrate 35g	

Exchanges: 2 starch, 1 vegetable, 3-1/2 lean meat

Tip

This tasty chicken sandwich is delicious served with corn on the cob and black olives. For a super-fast meal on a cold night, serve it with 5-Minute Soup (page 134).

Moroccan Lentil & Vegetable Soup

Cream of Chicken Soup

1 cup uncooked white rice
3 cans (about 14 ounces each) fat-free reduced-sodium chicken broth
1 bone-in chicken breast half (about 6 ounces)
1 stalk celery, chopped
1 carrot, thinly sliced
1/4 cup chopped onion
1-1/4 cups evaporated skimmed milk
1/4 teaspoon dried thyme leaves
1/8 teaspoon white pepper
1/8 teaspoon ground nutmeg
2 tablespoons finely chopped fresh parsley
1 green onion, finely chopped

1. Cook rice according to package directions, omitting salt.

2. Meanwhile, combine chicken broth and chicken in large saucepan. Bring to a boil over high heat. Reduce heat to medium-low. Simmer 10 minutes. Add celery, carrot and onion. Simmer 10 minutes or until chicken is no longer pink near bone and vegetables are tender.

3. Remove chicken breast from saucepan. Let stand 10 minutes or until cool enough to handle. Remove chicken from bone. Cut into 1-inch pieces.

4. Add rice, chicken pieces, milk, thyme, pepper and nutmeg to saucepan. Cook over medium-high heat 8 minutes or until soup thickens, stirring constantly.

5. Top each serving with chopped parsley and green onion.   *Makes 6 servings*

Nutrients per Serving: 1 cup soup

Calories 185	**Fiber** 1g
Fat <1g (sat <1g)	**Cholesterol** 13mg
Protein 12g	**Sodium** 532mg
Carbohydrate 33g	

Exchanges: 1-1/2 starch, 1/2 milk, 1 vegetable, 1/2 lean meat

Squash Bisque with Dill

Quick Recipe

2 boxes (12 ounces each) BIRDS EYE® frozen Cooked Winter Squash
2 cups skim milk, divided
1 tablespoon all-purpose flour
1 teaspoon dill weed
1/2 teaspoon chicken bouillon granules
Salt and black pepper to taste

• In medium saucepan, cook squash according to package directions.

• Stir in 1 cup milk, flour, dill and bouillon.

• Cook over medium-high heat until heated through, stirring frequently. Season with salt and pepper.

• Stir in additional milk to obtain desired consistency; heat through.   *Makes 4 servings*

Nutrients per Serving: 1 cup bisque (without salt and black pepper)

Calories 184	**Fiber** 5g
Fat 4g (sat 1g)	**Cholesterol** 5mg
Protein 10g	**Sodium** 79mg
Carbohydrate 29g	

Exchanges: 1 starch, 1/2 milk

Tip

Winter squash is packed with nutrients. Like carrots and sweet potatoes, it gets its bright color from beta carotene. Unlike some kinds of vegetables, winter squash, carrots and sweet potatoes get more nutritious as they are cooked—the beta carotene is converted to vitamin A during cooking. Beta carotene is also found in other deeply colored yellow, orange and green fruits and vegetables.

Pasta Meatball Soup

(Pictured at bottom right)

10 ounces 95% lean ground beef

5 tablespoons uncooked acini di pepe pasta,* divided

1/4 cup fresh bread crumbs

1 egg

2 tablespoons finely chopped fresh parsley, divided

1 teaspoon dried basil, divided

1/4 teaspoon salt

1/8 teaspoon black pepper

1 clove garlic, minced

2 cans (about 14 ounces each) reduced-fat reduced-sodium beef broth

1 can (8 ounces) tomato sauce

1/3 cup chopped onion

Acini di pepe is tiny rice-shaped pasta. Orzo or pastina can be substituted.

1. Combine beef, 2 tablespoons pasta, bread crumbs, egg, 1 tablespoon parsley, 1/2 teaspoon basil, salt, pepper and garlic in medium bowl. Shape into approximately 28 to 30 meatballs.

2. Bring broth, tomato sauce, onion and remaining 1/2 teaspoon basil to a boil in large saucepan over medium-high heat. Carefully add meatballs to broth. Reduce heat to medium-low; simmer, covered, 20 minutes. Add remaining 3 tablespoons pasta; cook 10 minutes or until tender. Garnish with remaining 1 tablespoon parsley.   *Makes 4 servings*

Nutrients per Serving: 1-1/2 cups soup

Calories 216	**Fiber** 1g
Fat 7g (sat 2g)	**Cholesterol** 89mg
Protein 22g	**Sodium** 599mg
Carbohydrate 15g	

Exchanges: 1 starch, 2-1/2 lean meat

Hometown Burgers

Quick Recipe

1 pound 95% lean ground beef

3/4 cup thinly sliced mushrooms

1/4 cup finely chopped onion

1/4 teaspoon salt

1/8 teaspoon black pepper

1/3 cup barbecue sauce

4 hamburger buns, split and toasted

4 lettuce leaves

4 slices tomato

4 slices onion

1. Prepare grill for direct grilling. Combine beef, mushrooms, chopped onion, salt and pepper in large bowl. Shape into 4 equal-size patties.

2. Grill, covered, over medium heat 8 to 10 minutes (or uncovered 13 to 15 minutes) or until no longer pink in centers, turning once and brushing often with barbecue sauce (do not brush with sauce during last 5 minutes of grilling). Place patties on buns with lettuce, tomato and sliced onion.   *Makes 4 servings*

Nutrients per Serving: 1 sandwich

Calories 309	**Fiber** 2g
Fat 8g (sat 3g)	**Cholesterol** 70mg
Protein 30g	**Sodium** 601mg
Carbohydrate 28g	

Exchanges: 2 starch, 3 lean meat

Pasta Meatball Soup

Desserts

⁊ ⁊ ⁊

Cinnamon Fruit Crisp

(Pictured at left)

> 4 medium unpeeled nectarines (about 1-1/2 pounds)
> 2 large unpeeled plums (about 8 ounces)
> 5 tablespoons sugar substitute,* divided
> 1-1/2 teaspoons ground cinnamon, divided
> 1/4 cup all-purpose flour
> 1/4 cup uncooked old-fashioned oats
> 3 tablespoons cold butter, cut into chunks
> 1/4 cup chopped pecans, toasted**

This recipe was tested with sucralose-based sugar substitute.

**Spread nuts in shallow baking pan. Bake in preheated 350ºF oven 5 to 10 minutes or until fragrant, stirring occasionally.*

1. Preheat oven to 375°F.

2. Slice nectarines and plums; reserve any accumulated juices. Place fruit slices and juice in large bowl. Combine 2 tablespoons sugar substitute and 1 teaspoon cinnamon in small bowl; sprinkle over fruit. Mix well. Transfer fruit mixture to 9-inch pie plate.

3. Combine flour, oats, remaining 3 tablespoons sugar substitute and remaining 1/2 teaspoon cinnamon in small bowl. Cut in butter with pastry blender or two knives until mixture resembles coarse crumbs. Stir in pecans; sprinkle oat mixture over fruit mixture.

4. Bake 30 minutes or until filling is bubbling and topping is golden brown. Serve warm.   *Makes 6 servings*

Nutrients per Serving: 1/2 cup

Calories 177	**Fiber** 3g
Fat 10g (sat 4g)	**Cholesterol** 15mg
Protein 3g	**Sodium** 41mg
Carbohydrate 24g	

Exchanges: 1/2 starch, 1 fruit, 2 fat

***Clockwise from top left:** Enlightened Banana Upside-Down Cake (page 155), Cinnamon Fruit Crisp, Peppermint Ice Cream Pie, (page 152) and Lattice-Topped Deep-Dish Cherry Pie (page 156)*

Caribbean Cake Squares

(Pictured at right)

1 package (9 ounces) single-layer yellow
   cake mix
2 egg whites
1/2 cup orange juice
2 cans (8 ounces each) crushed pineapple
   in juice
   Additional orange juice
1 tablespoon cornstarch
1/2 cup slivered almonds
1/2 cup flaked coconut
2 large ripe bananas
1 can (15 ounces) mandarin oranges,
   drained

1. Preheat oven to 350°F. Spray 13×9-inch
baking pan with nonstick cooking spray.

2. Beat cake mix, egg whites and orange juice
in medium bowl with electric mixer at medium
speed 2 minutes or until well blended. Spread
batter evenly in prepared pan.

3. Bake 11 to 12 minutes or until toothpick
inserted into center comes out clean. Cool
completely on wire rack.

4. Drain pineapple juice into 2-cup measure;
add additional orange juice to measure 1-1/2
cups liquid. Stir in cornstarch until smooth. Pour
juice mixture into medium saucepan; bring to
a boil over high heat, stirring constantly. Boil
1 minute, stirring constantly. Remove from heat.

5. Place almonds and coconut in 12-inch skillet;
heat over medium heat until almonds and
coconut are light brown, stirring frequently. Set
aside.

6. Spread pineapple evenly over cake. Slice
bananas and arrange over pineapple. Top with
mandarin oranges. Carefully drizzle juice
mixture evenly over topping. Sprinkle with
almond mixture. Cover; refrigerate 1 to 4 hours.
Cut into 16 pieces.   *Makes 16 servings*

Nutrients per Serving: 1 piece

Calories 148	**Fiber** 2g
Fat 5g (sat 1g)	**Cholesterol** <1mg
Protein 2g	**Sodium** 115mg
Carbohydrate 25g	

Exchanges: 1-1/2 starch, 1 fat

❧ ❧ ❧

Peppermint Ice Cream Pie

(Pictured on page 150)

4 cups sugar-free vanilla ice cream
6 sugar-free peppermint candies
1 reduced-fat graham cracker pie crust
1/4 cup sugar-free chocolate syrup
   Additional sugar-free peppermint
   candies (optional)

1. Scoop ice cream into medium bowl; let stand
at room temperature 5 minutes or until softened,
stirring occasionally.

2. Place 6 candies in heavy-duty food storage
bag; coarsely crush with rolling pin or meat
mallet. Stir candy into ice cream; spread evenly
in pie crust.

3. Cover; freeze at least 4 hours or overnight.
Using sharp knife that has been dipped in warm
water, cut pie into 12 slices. Transfer to serving
plates; drizzle with chocolate syrup. Garnish
with additional candies, if desired.

                              Makes 12 servings

Nutrients per Serving: 1 slice pie (1/12 of total recipe)

Calories 148	**Fiber** <1g
Fat 5g (sat 2g)	**Cholesterol** 8mg
Protein 3g	**Sodium** 104mg
Carbohydrate 25g	

Exchanges: 1-1/2 starch, 1/2 fat

4. Arrange crêpes, folded in quarters, on serving dish. Spoon sauce evenly over top. Serve immediately. *Makes 12 servings*

Crêpes

1 cup fat-free (skim) milk
2 egg whites
1/2 cup whole wheat flour
1/4 cup all-purpose flour
1 tablespoon sugar
1/8 teaspoon salt
1-1/2 teaspoons margarine

1. Combine milk, egg whites, both flours, sugar and salt in food processor or blender; process until well blended. Pour mixture into large bowl.

2. Melt margarine in nonstick crêpe or omelet pan over medium heat. Pour melted margarine into crêpe batter; mix well. Wipe pan with paper towel; save towel for later use. Heat pan over medium heat.

3. Spoon 2 tablespoons batter into hot pan; tilt to coat entire pan surface. When edges of batter curl away from sides of pan, flip crêpe. Cook until brown.

4. Repeat with remaining batter; wipe pan with reserved paper towel between each crêpe.
Makes 12 crêpes

Nutrients per Serving: 1 crêpe with about 1/4 cup strawberry sauce

Calories 94	**Fiber** 1g
Fat 1g (sat 0g)	**Cholesterol** 0mg
Protein 2g	**Sodium** 52mg
Carbohydrate 17g	

Exchanges: 1/2 starch, 1/2 fruit, 1/2 fat

Strawberry Crêpes Suzette

Strawberry Crêpes Suzette

(Pictured above)

1 cup fresh orange juice
2 teaspoons cornstarch
2 tablespoons sugar
2 teaspoons grated orange peel
3 cups fresh strawberry slices
1/4 cup orange-flavored liqueur
1 teaspoon margarine
12 Crêpes (recipe follows)

1. Combine orange juice and cornstarch in large saucepan. Stir until cornstarch is dissolved.

2. Add sugar, grated orange peel and strawberries; mix well. Bring to a boil over medium heat. Reduce heat to low and simmer, stirring until slightly thickened. Remove from heat; stir in liqueur and margarine.

3. Prepare crêpes.

Amy's Lemonade Mousse

Quick Recipe

4 cups cold fat-free (skim) milk
2 packages (1 ounce each) fat-free sugar-free vanilla instant pudding mix
2 packages (1/2 ounce each) sugar-free powdered lemonade mix, undiluted
1 container (8 ounces) fat-free whipped topping
Fresh or frozen mixed berries (optional)

1. Pour milk into large bowl. Add pudding mix and whisk 2 minutes until smooth.

2. Whisk in powdered lemonade mix. When mixture thickens, whisk in whipped topping until smooth. Pour into 8 parfait glasses. Chill.

3. Garnish with berries, if desired.

Makes 8 servings

Nutrients per Serving: about 2/3 cup mousse

Calories 120
Fat <1g (sat <1g)
Protein 4g
Carbohydrate 21g
Fiber 0g
Cholesterol 2mg
Sodium 405mg

Exchanges: 1 starch, 1/2 milk

Tip

When purchasing fresh strawberries for Strawberry Crêpes Suzette, choose those that are bright red and still have their green stems attached. Don't wash them until you are ready to use them. Store strawberries in a moisture-proof container in the refrigerator for 2 to 3 days.

Enlightened Banana Upside-Down Cake

(Pictured on page 150)

1/2 cup sugar
1 tablespoon water
2 tablespoons butter
2 small bananas, sliced 1/4 inch thick
1-1/2 cups all-purpose flour
2 teaspoons baking powder
1/2 teaspoon salt
3/4 cup sugar substitute*
1/4 cup canola oil
1/4 cup unsweetened applesauce
3 egg whites
1 egg yolk
1/2 cup low-fat buttermilk
1 teaspoon vanilla extract

*This recipe was tested with sucralose-based sugar substitute.

1. Preheat oven to 325°F.

2. Combine sugar and water in small saucepan. Heat mixture over medium-high heat, stirring mixture and swirling pan, until mixture is amber in color. Stir in butter. Immediately pour mixture into 9-inch square baking pan. Arrange banana slices in sugar mixture.

3. Sift flour, baking powder and salt in medium bowl; set aside. Beat sugar substitute, oil and applesauce in large bowl with electric mixer at medium speed 1 minute. Beat in egg whites and yolk, one at a time, until blended. Add buttermilk and vanilla. Gradually add flour mixture, beating 1 minute or until blended.

4. Pour batter over bananas in pan. Bake 30 to 35 minutes or until toothpick inserted into center comes out clean. Cool 5 minutes in pan on wire rack; invert onto serving plate. Cool slightly; cut into 12 pieces. Serve warm or at room temperature.

Makes 12 servings

Nutrients per Serving: 1 piece cake

Calories 184
Fat 7g (sat 2g)
Protein 3g
Carbohydrate 27g
Fiber 1g
Cholesterol 23mg
Sodium 191mg

Exchanges: 1-1/2 starch, 1/2 fruit, 1 fat

Individual No-Bake Cheesecake Fruit Cups

(Pictured at right)

- **1 cup quartered strawberries**
- **1 cup diced peaches**
- **3 tablespoons sugar substitute,* divided**
- **1/4 teaspoon ground ginger**
- **5 ounces reduced-fat cream cheese, softened**
- **3 tablespoons fat-free sour cream**
- **2 tablespoons fat-free (skim) milk**
- **1 teaspoon vanilla extract**
- **1/4 cup graham cracker crumbs**

*This recipe was tested with sucralose-based sugar substitute.

1. Combine strawberries, peaches, 1 tablespoon sugar substitute and ginger in medium bowl. Toss gently to blend. Set aside.

2. Beat cream cheese, sour cream, milk, vanilla and remaining 2 tablespoons sugar substitute in small bowl with electric mixer at medium speed until smooth.

3. Place about 3 tablespoons cream cheese mixture in each of four (4-ounce) ramekins.* Sprinkle 1 tablespoon cracker crumbs evenly into each cup. Top with 1/2 cup berry mixture. Cover and refrigerate at least 1 hour.

Makes 4 servings

*Note: If ramekins are not available, you may substitute custard dishes or 4 muffin cups lined with foil liners.

Nutrients per Serving: 1 cheesecake cup

Calories 115	**Fiber** 2g
Fat 4g (sat 12g)	**Cholesterol** 12mg
Protein 4g	**Sodium** 162mg
Carbohydrate 17g	

Exchanges: 1/2 starch, 1/2 fruit, 1 fat

Lattice-Topped Deep-Dish Cherry Pie

low sodium

(Pictured on page 150)

- **2 cans (about 16 ounces each) pitted tart red cherries in light syrup**
- **1/2 cup sugar substitute***
- **3 tablespoons quick-cooking tapioca**
- **1/4 teaspoon almond extract**
- **3/4 cup all-purpose flour**
- **1/4 teaspoon salt**
- **3 tablespoons shortening**
- **2 to 3 tablespoons cold water**

*This recipe was tested with sucralose-based sugar substitute.

1. Preheat oven to 375°F. Drain one can of cherries. Combine drained cherries, undrained cherries, sugar substitute, tapioca and almond extract in large bowl; set aside.

2. Combine flour and salt in small bowl. Cut in shortening with pastry blender or two knives until mixture resembles fine crumbs. Add water, 1 tablespoon at a time, stirring just until dough is moistened. Shape dough into ball. Roll dough into 9×8-inch rectangle on lightly floured surface. Cut into 9 (8×1-inch) strips.

3. Spoon cherry mixture in 13×9-inch baking dish. Place 4 pastry strips on a diagonal over cherry mixture. Weave remaining 5 pastry strips diagonally across first layer; trim. Pinch strips at ends to seal. Bake 40 to 50 minutes or until filling is bubbly and pastry is lightly browned. Remove to wire rack; cool slightly. Spoon into bowls to serve. *Makes 9 servings*

Nutrients per Serving: 2/3 cup pie

Calories 132	**Fiber** 1g
Fat 4g (sat 1g)	**Cholesterol** 0mg
Protein 2g	**Sodium** 73mg
Carbohydrate 22g	

Exchanges: 1/2 starch, 1 fruit, 1 fat

Individual No-Bake Cheesecake Fruit Cups

Peanut Butter Bear

Peanut Butter Bears

 _{low sodium}

(Pictured above)

2 cups uncooked quick oats
2 cups all-purpose flour
1 tablespoon baking powder
1 cup granulated sugar
3/4 cup (1-1/2 sticks) butter, softened
1/2 cup creamy peanut butter
1/2 cup packed brown sugar
1/2 cup cholesterol-free egg substitute *or* 2 eggs
1 teaspoon vanilla extract
3 tablespoons miniature semisweet chocolate chips

1. Combine oats, flour and baking powder in large bowl; set aside.

2. Beat granulated sugar, butter, peanut butter and brown sugar in large bowl with electric mixer at medium-high speed until well blended. Add egg substitute and vanilla; beat until light and fluffy. Add oat mixture; beat at low speed until combined. Wrap dough in plastic wrap. Refrigerate 1 to 2 hours or until easy to handle.

3. Preheat oven to 375°F.

4. For each bear, shape 1 (1-inch) ball for body and 1 (3/4-inch) ball for head. Place body and head together on cookie sheet; flatten slightly. Form 7 small balls for arms, ears, legs and nose; arrange on bear body and head. Place 2 chocolate chips on each head for eyes. Place 1 chocolate chip on each body for belly button.

5. Bake 9 to 11 minutes or until edges are lightly browned. Cool 1 minute on cookie sheet. Remove to wire racks; cool completely.

Makes 4 dozen cookies

Nutrients per Serving: 1 cookie

Calories 110	**Fiber** 1g
Fat 5g (sat 2g)	**Cholesterol** 15mg
Protein 2g	**Sodium** 82mg
Carbohydrate 14g	

Exchanges: 1 starch, 1 fat

Cinnamon Compote

_{low fat} _{low sodium} _{cooking for 1 or 2}

Quick Recipe

1/2 cup unsweetened pineapple juice
1/8 teaspoon ground cinnamon
1-1/2 cups cubed cantaloupe
1/2 cup blueberries

1. Combine juice and cinnamon in small saucepan. Cook and stir over low heat 4 to 5 minutes or until slightly syrupy. Cool slightly.

2. Combine cantaloupe and blueberries in medium bowl. Pour juice mixture over fruit; toss. Refrigerate until cold.

Makes 2 servings

Nutrients per Serving: 1 cup compote

Calories 98	**Fiber** 2g
Fat 1g (sat <1g)	**Cholesterol** 0mg
Protein 2g	**Sodium** 14mg
Carbohydrate 24g	

Exchanges: 1-1/2 fruit

Dessert Nachos

Quick Recipe (Pictured at bottom right)

    3 (6-inch) flour tortillas
      Nonstick cooking spray
    1 tablespoon sugar
  1/8 teaspoon ground cinnamon
      Dash ground allspice
    1 cup (8 ounces) vanilla sugar-free
      fat-free yogurt
    1 teaspoon grated orange peel
1-1/2 cups strawberries
  1/2 cup blueberries
    4 teaspoons miniature semisweet
      chocolate chips

1. Preheat oven to 375°F.

2. Cut each tortilla into 8 wedges. Place on ungreased baking sheet. Generously spray tortilla wedges with cooking spray. Combine sugar, cinnamon and allspice in small bowl. Sprinkle over tortilla wedges. Bake 7 to 9 minutes or until lightly browned; cool completely.

3. Meanwhile, combine yogurt and orange peel. Stem strawberries; cut lengthwise into quarters.

4. Place 6 tortilla wedges on each of 4 small plates. Top with strawberries and blueberries. Spoon yogurt mixture on top. Sprinkle with chocolate chips. Serve immediately.

Makes 4 servings

Nutrients per Serving: 6 tortilla wedges with 1/2 cup berries, 1/4 cup yogurt mixture and 1 teaspoon chocolate chips

Calories 160	**Fiber** 3g
Fat 3g (sat 1g)	**Cholesterol** 2mg
Protein 4g	**Sodium** 146mg
Carbohydrate 28g	

Exchanges: 1 starch, 1 fruit, 1/2 fat

Grapefruit Sorbet

    2 medium grapefruit
    2 tablespoons honey
      Water
    1 teaspoon chopped fresh mint

1. Peel grapefruit; divide into sections and remove white membrane and seeds. Place grapefruit in food processor; process until smooth. Pour grapefruit into 4-cup measure; add honey and enough water to equal 2 cups. Add mint; mix well.

2. Pour mixture into 9-inch square metal pan. Freeze about 1 hour or until mixture becomes slushy. Transfer mixture to bowl; beat with electric mixer until smooth. Return to pan; freeze 1 to 2 hours or until mixture is frozen.

Makes 4 servings

Nutrients per Serving: 1/2 cup sorbet

Calories 70	**Fiber** 2g
Fat <1g (sat 0g)	**Cholesterol** 0mg
Protein 1g	**Sodium** 1mg
Carbohydrate 18g	

Exchanges: 1/2 starch, 1/2 fruit

Dessert Nachos

Strawberry-Banana Granité

(Pictured at right)

2 ripe medium bananas, peeled and sliced (about 2 cups)
2 cups unsweetened frozen strawberries (*do not thaw*)
3 tablespoons no-sugar-added strawberry fruit spread
1 tablespoon warm water
Whole fresh strawberries (optional)
Fresh mint leaves (optional)

1. Place banana slices in plastic bag; freeze until firm.

2. Place frozen banana slices and frozen strawberries in food processor. Let stand 10 minutes for fruit to soften slightly. Add fruit spread and warm water. Remove plunger from top of food processor to allow air to be incorporated. Process until smooth, scraping down sides of container frequently. Garnish with fresh strawberries and mint leaves, if desired. Serve immediately. Freeze leftovers.

Makes 5 servings

Note: Granité can be transferred to an airtight container and frozen up to 1 month. Let stand at room temperature 10 minutes to soften slightly before serving.

Nutrients per Serving: 2/3 cup granité

Calories 87	**Fiber** 2g
Fat <1g (sat <1g)	**Cholesterol** 0mg
Protein 1g	**Sodium** 2mg
Carbohydrate 22g	

Exchanges: 1-1/2 fruit

Mango Vanilla Parfaits

1/2 (4-serving-size) package vanilla sugar-free instant pudding mix
1-1/4 cups fat-free (skim) milk
1/2 cup cubed mango
2 large strawberries, sliced
3 sugar-free shortbread cookies, crumbled *or* 2 tablespoons reduced-fat granola
Strawberry slices (optional)

1. Prepare pudding according to package directions using 1-1/4 cups milk.

2. Layer one quarter of pudding, half of mango, half of strawberries and one quarter of pudding in parfait glass or small bowl. Repeat layers in second parfait glass. Refrigerate 30 minutes.

3. Just before serving, top with cookie crumbs and garnish with strawberry slices, if desired.

Makes 2 servings

Nutrients per Serving: 1 parfait (1/2 of total recipe)

Calories 153	**Fiber** 2g
Fat 1g (sat 1g)	**Cholesterol** 3mg
Protein 6g	**Sodium** 129mg
Carbohydrate 29g	

Exchanges: 1 starch, 1/2 fruit, 1/2 milk

Tip

When selecting fresh mangoes, look for those that are firm but not hard. They should yield slightly to pressure. The skin should be taut and smooth; black speckling is perfectly acceptable. Good mangoes will have a sweet, fruity aroma around the stem end.

Pineapple-Raisin Bars

        2 eggs
        1 cup thawed frozen unsweetened
            pineapple juice concentrate
        1/4 cup (1/2 stick) butter, melted
        1 teaspoon vanilla extract
    1-1/3 cups all-purpose flour
        2/3 cup uncooked old-fashioned oats
        1 teaspoon baking soda
        1/4 teaspoon salt
        1 teaspoon ground cinnamon
        1/2 teaspoon ground ginger
        1/8 teaspoon ground nutmeg
        1 can (8 ounces) crushed pineapple in
            unsweetened juice, well drained
        3/4 cup lightly toasted* chopped pecans
        1/2 cup golden raisins

*Spread nuts in shallow baking pan. Bake in preheated 350°F oven 5 to 10 minutes or until fragrant, stirring occasionally.

1. Preheat oven to 350°F. Spray 11×7-inch baking dish with nonstick cooking spray.

2. Beat eggs in large bowl. Blend in pineapple juice concentrate, butter and vanilla.

3. Combine flour, oats, baking soda, salt and spices in another large bowl. Stir into pineapple mixture; mix well. Stir in pineapple, pecans and raisins. Spread batter into prepared dish.

4. Bake 18 to 20 minutes or until firm. Cool completely on wire rack. Cut into 16 bars. Store in tightly covered container.

Makes 16 servings

Nutrients per Serving: 1 bar (1/16 of total recipe)

Calories 181	**Fiber** 2g
Fat 8g (sat 2g)	**Cholesterol** 35mg
Protein 3g	**Sodium** 156mg
Carbohydrate 26g	

Exchanges: 1 starch, 1/2 fruit, 1-1/2 fat

Orange Cranberry Cookies

Quick Recipe

        1/4 cup stick butter or margarine
        1 egg
        3 tablespoons frozen orange juice
            concentrate
        3/4 cup all-purpose flour, sifted
        1/3 cup EQUAL® SPOONFUL*
        1/4 cup quick oats, uncooked
        1 teaspoon grated orange peel
        1/4 teaspoon baking soda
        1/8 teaspoon cream of tartar
            Dash salt
        1/2 cup dried cranberries
        1/2 cup chopped walnuts

*May substitute 8 packets EQUAL® sweetener.

• Beat butter in medium bowl. Beat in egg and frozen orange juice concentrate.

• Combine flour, Equal®, oats, orange peel, baking soda, cream of tartar and salt in separate bowl.

• Add flour mixture to creamed mixture and mix well. Stir in cranberries and walnuts.

• Drop by rounded teaspoonfuls onto ungreased baking sheet.

• Bake in preheated 375°F oven 8 to 10 minutes or until bottoms are lightly browned. Cool on wire racks.

Makes 24 cookies

Nutrients per Serving: 1 cookie

Calories 66	**Fiber** 1g
Fat 4g (sat 2g)	**Cholesterol** 14mg
Protein 1g	**Sodium** 30mg
Carbohydrate 7g	

Exchanges: 1/2 starch, 1/2 fat

No-Bake Cherry Cake

Quick Recipe   *(Pictured below)*

   1 (10-inch) prepared angel food cake
1-1/2 cups fat-free (skim) milk
   1 cup light sour cream
   1 package (4-serving size) fat-free sugar-free vanilla instant pudding mix
   1 can (21 ounces) light cherry pie filling

1. Tear cake into bite-sized pieces; press into 11×17-inch baking dish.

2. Combine milk, sour cream and pudding mix in medium bowl; beat 2 minutes or until thick. Spread over cake.

3. Spoon cherry pie filling evenly over top of cake. Chill until ready to serve.

Makes 12 servings

Nutrients per Serving: 1 piece (1/12 of total recipe)

Calories 156
Fat 2g (sat 1g)
Protein 4g
Carbohydrate 31g
Fiber 1g
Cholesterol 7mg
Sodium 326mg

Exchanges: 2 starch

No-Bake Cherry Cake

Angelic Cupcakes

(Pictured at right)

1 package (16 ounces) angel food cake mix
1-1/4 cups cold water
1/4 teaspoon peppermint extract (optional)
Red food coloring
4-1/2 cups reduced-fat whipped topping

1. Preheat oven to 375°F. Line 36 standard (2-1/2-inch) muffin cups with paper baking cups.

2. Beat cake mix, water and peppermint extract, if desired, in large bowl with electric mixer at low speed 30 seconds. Beat 1 minute more.

3. Pour half of batter into medium bowl; carefully stir in 9 drops red food coloring. Alternate spoonfuls of white and pink batter in each prepared muffin cup, filling cups three-fourths full.

4. Bake 11 minutes or until cupcakes are golden with deep cracks on top. Remove to wire racks; cool completely.

5. Divide whipped topping between two small bowls. Add 2 drops red food coloring to one bowl of whipped topping; stir gently to reach desired shade. Frost cupcakes with pink or white whipped topping. Refrigerate leftovers.

Makes 36 cupcakes

Nutrients per Serving: 1 cupcake

Calories 68	**Fiber** 0g
Fat 1g (sat 1g)	**Cholesterol** 0mg
Protein 1g	**Sodium** 113mg
Carbohydrate 13g	

Exchanges: 1 starch

Baked Flan

low carb

4 cups 2% milk
6 eggs
1 cup plus 2 tablespoons EQUAL® SPOONFUL*
2-1/2 teaspoons vanilla
1/4 teaspoon salt
Sliced fresh fruit (optional)
Fresh mint (optional)

*May substitute 27 packets EQUAL® sweetener.

• Heat milk just to simmering in medium saucepan. Let cool 5 minutes.

• Beat eggs, Equal®, vanilla and salt in large bowl until smooth. Gradually beat in hot milk. Pour mixture into 1-1/2-quart casserole or ten 6-ounce custard cups.

• Place casserole or custard cups in roasting pan. Pour 1 inch of hot water into roasting pan. Bake in preheated 325°F oven 50 to 60 minutes or until knife inserted halfway between center and edge of custard comes out clean.

• Remove casserole or custard cups from roasting pan. Cool to room temperature on wire rack. Refrigerate several hours until well chilled.

• Serve garnished with sliced fresh fruit and mint, if desired. *Makes 10 servings*

Nutrients per Serving: 1/2 cup flan

Calories 106	**Fiber** 0g
Fat 5g (sat 2g)	**Cholesterol** 135mg
Protein 7g	**Sodium** 145mg
Carbohydrate 8g	

Exchanges: 1/2 milk, 1/2 lean meat, 1 fat

Cherry Bowl Cheesecake

Cherry Bowl Cheesecakes

(Pictured above)

1 package (8 ounces) fat-free cream cheese, softened
1 package (8 ounces) reduced-fat cream cheese, softened
2 tablespoons fat-free (skim) milk
4 packets sugar substitute*
1/4 teaspoon almond extract
40 reduced-fat vanilla wafers
1 can (21 ounces) light cherry pie filling

*This recipe was tested with sucralose-based sugar substitute.

1. Beat cream cheese, milk, sugar substitute and almond extract in medium bowl with electric mixer at high speed until well blended.

2. Place one vanilla wafer on bottom of 4-ounce ramekin.* Arrange four additional vanilla wafers around side of ramekin. Repeat with remaining wafers. Fill each ramekin with 1/4 cup cream cheese mixture; top each with 1/4 cup cherry pie filling. Cover with plastic wrap; refrigerate 8 hours or overnight.   *Makes 8 servings*

Variation: If ramekins are not available, you may substitute custard dishes or 8 muffin cups lined with foil liners.

Nutrients per Serving: 1 cheesecake

Calories 217	**Fiber** 1g
Fat 9g (sat 4g)	**Cholesterol** 28mg
Protein 9g	**Sodium** 312mg
Carbohydrate 27g	

Exchanges: 2 starch, 1/2 lean meat, 1 fat

ᔐ ᔐ ᔐ

Poached Pears in Cinnamon-Apricot Sauce

low fat   low sodium

Quick Recipe

1 can (5-1/2 ounces) apricot nectar
1 tablespoon sugar
1 teaspoon lemon juice
1/2 teaspoon ground cinnamon
1/4 teaspoon grated lemon peel
1/8 teaspoon ground cloves
2 large pears

1. Combine apricot nectar, sugar, lemon juice, cinnamon, lemon peel and cloves in large skillet. Bring to a boil over medium-high heat.

2. Meanwhile, cut pears lengthwise into halves, leaving stem attached to one half. Remove cores. Cut pears lengthwise into thin slices, taking care not to cut through stem end. Add pears to skillet with nectar mixture; bring to a boil over medium-high heat. Reduce heat to medium-low. Simmer, covered, 6 to 8 minutes or until pears are just tender. Carefully remove pears from skillet, reserving liquid.

3. Simmer liquid in skillet, uncovered, over medium heat 2 to 3 minutes or until mixture thickens slightly, stirring occasionally. Fan out pears; spoon sauce over pears. Serve pears warmed or chilled.   *Makes 4 servings*

Nutrients per Serving: 1/2 pear with about 1/2 cup sauce

Calories 84	**Fiber** 3g
Fat <1g (sat <1g)	**Cholesterol** 0mg
Protein 1g	**Sodium** 1mg
Carbohydrate 22g	

Exchanges: 1-1/2 fruit

Strawberry-Peach Cream Puffs

(Pictured on front cover)

3/4 cup water

3 tablespoons butter

3/4 cup all-purpose flour

3 eggs

1 quart strawberries, stemmed and quartered

1-1/2 cups diced peaches or nectarines

6 packets sugar substitute*

1/4 to 1/2 teaspoon vanilla extract

1/8 to 1/4 teaspoon almond extract

2 cups fat-free vanilla ice cream

1 tablespoon powdered sugar

This recipe was tested with sucralose-based sugar substitute.

1. Preheat oven to 400°F. Combine water and butter in medium saucepan. Bring to a boil over high heat. Reduce heat to low; stir in flour until well blended. Remove from heat. Stir in eggs, one at a time, until well blended.

2. Drop batter by 1/3 cupfuls onto ungreased baking sheet. Bake 35 minutes or until golden brown. Cool completely on baking sheet on wire rack.

3. Combine strawberries, peaches, sugar substitute, vanilla and almond extract in medium bowl. Place 3/4 cup strawberry mixture in food processor or blender; process until smooth. Stir into remaining strawberry mixture; set aside.

4. Cut each puff in half width wise. Spoon 1/4 cup ice cream on bottom half of each puff. Top with 1/2 cup strawberry mixture and top half of puff. Sprinkle with powdered sugar. Serve immediately. *Makes 8 servings*

Nutrients per Serving: 1 cream puff

Calories 197
Fat 7g (sat 4g)
Protein 6g
Carbohydrate 31g
Fiber 4g
Cholesterol 93mg
Sodium 82mg

Exchanges: 1 starch, 1 fruit, 1/2 lean meat, 1 fat

Brownies

1/2 cup boiling water

1/2 cup unsweetened cocoa powder

1-1/4 cups all-purpose flour

3/4 cup granulated sugar

3/4 cup packed light brown sugar

4 egg whites, lightly beaten

1/3 cup canola oil

1-1/2 teaspoons vanilla extract

1 teaspoon baking powder

1/4 teaspoon salt

1/2 cup chopped unsalted mixed nuts (optional)

1. Preheat oven to 350°F. Spray 13×9-inch baking pan with nonstick cooking spray.

2. Whisk boiling water and cocoa in large heatproof bowl. Stir in flour, granulated sugar, brown sugar, egg whites, oil, vanilla, baking powder and salt; mix well. Fold in chopped nuts, if desired.

3. Pour mixture into prepared pan. Bake 25 minutes or until brownies spring back when lightly touched. *Do not overbake.* Cool in pan on wire rack; cut into 32 pieces.
Makes 32 brownies

Nutrients per Serving: 1 brownie (1/32 of total recipe)

Calories 81
Fat 2g (sat <1g)
Protein 1g
Carbohydrate 14g
Fiber 0g
Cholesterol 0mg
Sodium 37mg

Exchanges: 1 starch, 1/2 fat

Cocoa Hazelnut Macaroons

low fat | low sodium

(Pictured at right)

1/3 cup hazelnuts
3/4 cup uncooked quick oats
6 tablespoons unsweetened cocoa powder
1/3 cup packed light brown sugar
2 tablespoons all-purpose flour
4 egg whites
1 teaspoon vanilla extract
1/2 teaspoon salt
1/3 cup plus 1 tablespoon granulated sugar

1. Preheat oven to 375°F. Spread hazelnuts in even layer on baking sheet. Bake 8 minutes or until lightly browned. Quickly transfer nuts to clean dry dish towel. Fold towel; rub vigorously to remove as much of the skins as possible. Cool completely. Finely chop nuts. Combine chopped nuts, oats, cocoa, brown sugar and flour in medium bowl; mix well.

2. *Reduce oven temperature to 325°F.* Combine egg whites, vanilla and salt in clean dry medium mixing bowl. Beat with electric mixer at high speed until soft peaks form. Gradually add granulated sugar; beat at high speed until stiff peaks form. Gently fold in nut mixture with rubber spatula.

3. Drop level measuring tablespoonfuls of dough onto ungreased cookie sheet. Bake 15 to 17 minutes or until tops of cookies no longer appear wet. Transfer to wire rack. Store in airtight container. *Makes 3 dozen cookies*

Nutrients per Serving: 3 macaroons

Calories 104	**Fiber** 1g
Fat 3g (sat <1g)	**Cholesterol** <1mg
Protein 3g	**Sodium** 112mg
Carbohydrate 18g	

Exchanges: 1 starch, 1/2 fat

Quick Cinnamon Apple Dessert

low fat | low sodium |

Quick Recipe

1/2 large Granny Smith apple, cored and thinly sliced
1 tablespoon lemon juice
2 teaspoons spoonable brown sugar substitute*
1/4 teaspoon cinnamon
1/2 teaspoon vanilla extract
1 teaspoon raisins
2 tablespoons fat-free whipped topping

This recipe was tested with sucralose-based sugar substitute.

Microwave Directions

1. Toss apple slices with lemon juice, brown sugar substitute, cinnamon and vanilla in medium bowl.

2. Lightly spray microwavable dish with nonstick cooking spray. Sprinkle raisins in dish. Arrange apple slices in a spiral pattern over raisins. Spoon any juices in bowl over apples.

3. Cover with waxed paper; microwave on HIGH 3 minutes. Let stand, covered, 5 minutes.

4. Serve warm or at room temperature with whipped topping. *Makes 2 servings*

Note: This recipe was tested in an 1100-watt microwave oven.

Nutrients per Serving: 1/2 dessert

Calories 80	**Fiber** 2g
Fat <1g (sat <1g)	**Cholesterol** 0mg
Protein <1g	**Sodium** 9mg
Carbohydrate 19g	

Exchanges: 1 fruit

Banana Chocolate Cupcakes

(Pictured above)

2 cups all-purpose flour
3/4 cup sugar, divided
1/4 cup unsweetened cocoa powder
3/4 teaspoon baking soda
1/2 teaspoon baking powder
1/4 teaspoon salt
1 cup (8 ounces) plain or banana-flavored low-fat yogurt
1/2 cup mashed ripe banana (1 medium banana)
1/3 cup canola oil
1/4 cup fat-free (skim) milk
2 teaspoons vanilla extract
3 egg whites

1. Preheat oven to 350°F. Line 20 standard (2-1/2-inch) muffin cups with foil baking cups.

2. Combine flour, 1/4 cup sugar, cocoa, baking soda, baking powder and salt in large bowl; set aside.

3. Mix yogurt, banana, oil, milk and vanilla in small bowl until well blended.

4. Beat egg whites in small deep bowl with electric mixer at medium speed until foamy. Gradually add remaining 1/2 cup sugar, beating well after each addition, until sugar is dissolved and stiff peaks form.

5. Stir yogurt mixture into flour mixture just until dry ingredients are moistened. Gently fold in one third of egg white mixture until blended; fold in remaining egg white mixture. Spoon batter into prepared muffin cups, filling two-thirds full.

6. Bake 20 to 25 minutes or until toothpick inserted into centers comes out clean.

7. Remove cupcakes to wire racks; cool completely. Store in airtight container at room temperature. *Makes 20 cupcakes*

Nutrients per Serving: 1 cupcake

Calories 138	**Fiber** <1g
Fat 4g (sat <1g)	**Cholesterol** 1mg
Protein 3g	**Sodium** 109mg
Carbohydrate 23g	

Exchanges: 1-1/2 starch, 1/2 fat

Raspberry Smoothies

Quick Recipe

1-1/2 cups fresh or frozen raspberries
1 cup (8 ounces) plain sugar-free fat-free yogurt
1 cup crushed ice
1 tablespoon honey
2 packets sugar substitute*

This recipe was tested with sucralose-based sugar substitute.

Place all ingredients in food processor or blender; process until smooth. Serve immediately. *Makes 2 servings*

Nutrients per Serving: 1-1/2 cups smoothie

Calories 143	**Fiber** 6g
Fat <1g (sat <1g)	**Cholesterol** 2mg
Protein 8g	**Sodium** 88mg
Carbohydrate 28g	

Exchanges: 1/2 starch, 1 fruit, 1/2 milk

Tip

Overripe bananas add more flavor to baked goods than perfectly ripe bananas. When selecting a banana for the Banana Chocolate Cupcakes, look for an overripe banana with lots of speckling on its skin. Or, buy a ripe banana and let it stand at room temperature for a few days until it is overripe.

Thumbprint Cookies

(Pictured at bottom right)

- **1-1/2 cups all-purpose flour**
- **1 teaspoon baking soda**
- **1/4 teaspoon salt**
- **2/3 cup sugar**
- **1/4 cup (1/2 stick) butter, softened**
- **1 egg white**
- **1 teaspoon vanilla extract**
- **1/2 cup raspberry or apricot fruit spread**

1. Combine flour, baking soda and salt in medium bowl; set aside. Beat sugar, butter, egg white and vanilla in large bowl with electric mixer at high speed until blended. Add flour mixture; mix well. Press mixture together to form ball. Cover with plastic wrap. Refrigerate 30 minutes or overnight.

2. Preheat oven to 375°F. Spray cookie sheet with nonstick cooking spray.

3. With lightly floured hands, shape dough into 20 (1-inch) balls; place on cookie sheet. Make indentation with thumb in center of each ball.

4. Bake 10 to 12 minutes or until golden brown. Remove to wire rack to cool. Fill each indentation with about 1 teaspoon fruit spread.

Makes 20 cookies

Nutrients per Serving: 1 cookie

Calories 98	**Fiber** <1g
Fat 2g (sat 1g)	**Cholesterol** 6mg
Protein 1g	**Sodium** 96mg
Carbohydrate 18g	

Exchanges: 1 starch, 1/2 fat

Strawberries with Honeyed Yogurt Sauce

Quick Recipe

- **1 quart fresh strawberries**
- **1 cup (8 ounces) plain low-fat yogurt**
- **1 tablespoon orange juice**
- **1 to 2 teaspoons honey**
- **Ground cinnamon**

Rinse and hull strawberries. Combine yogurt, juice, honey and cinnamon to taste in small bowl; mix well. Serve sauce over berries.

Makes 4 servings

Nutrients per Serving: 1 cup strawberries with about 1/4 cup sauce

Calories 88	**Fiber** 4g
Fat 1g (sat 1g)	**Cholesterol** 4mg
Protein 4g	**Sodium** 41mg
Carbohydrate 16g	

Exchanges: 1 fruit, 1/2 milk

Thumbprint Cookies

Three-Melon Soup

low fat   low sodium

(Pictured at right)

        3 cups cubed seeded watermelon
        3 tablespoons unsweetened pineapple
            juice
        2 tablespoons lemon juice
    1/4 cantaloupe melon
    1/8 honeydew melon
        Fresh mint sprigs (optional)

1. Combine watermelon, pineapple juice and lemon juice in blender; process until smooth. Chill at least 2 hours or overnight.

2. Scoop out balls of cantaloupe and honeydew.

3. To serve, pour watermelon mixture into shallow bowls; garnish with cantaloupe, honeydew and mint, if desired.

Makes 4 servings

Nutrients per Serving: about 1/2 cup soup

Calories 68	**Fiber** 1g
Fat 1g (sat <1g)	**Cholesterol** 0mg
Protein 1g	**Sodium** 9mg
Carbohydrate 16g	

Exchanges: 1 fruit

Tip

To save time, purchase precut melon from the produce section or salad bar at the grocery store. Avoid melon with coarse pale flesh, dark wet-looking flesh (overripe) or an abundance of small white seeds (underripe).

Coconut Custard Pie

        Pastry for single-crust 9-inch pie
        4 eggs
    1/4 teaspoon salt
        2 cups skim milk
    1/2 cup flaked coconut
    3/4 cup EQUAL® SPOONFUL*
        2 teaspoons coconut extract

*May substitute 18 packets EQUAL® sweetener.

• Roll pastry on floured surface into circle 1 inch larger than inverted 9-inch pie pan. Ease pastry into pan; trim and flute edge.

• Beat eggs and salt in large bowl about 5 minutes or until thick and lemon colored. Mix in milk and remaining ingredients. Pour mixture into pastry shell.

• Bake pie in preheated 425°F oven 15 minutes. Reduce oven temperature to 350°F; bake 20 to 25 minutes or until sharp knife inserted halfway between center and edge of pie comes out clean. Cool on wire rack. Serve at room temperature, or refrigerate and serve chilled.

Makes 8 servings

Tip: Never pour a filling into the pie shell until just before baking—letting the filling stand in an unbaked pie shell will lead to a soggy crust.

Nutrients per Serving: 1 slice pie (1/8 of total recipe)

Calories 223	**Fiber** 1g
Fat 13g (sat 5g)	**Cholesterol** 107mg
Protein 7g	**Sodium** 281mg
Carbohydrate 19g	

Exchanges: 1 starch, 1 lean meat, 2 fat

Berry-Peachy Cobbler

(Pictured at right)

- **4 tablespoons plus 2 teaspoons sugar, divided**
- **3/4 cup plus 2 tablespoons all-purpose flour, divided**
- **1-1/4 pounds peaches, peeled and sliced *or* 1 package (16 ounces) frozen unsweetened sliced peaches, thawed and drained**
- **2 cups fresh raspberries *or* 1 package (12 ounces) frozen unsweetened raspberries**
- **1 teaspoon grated lemon peel**
- **1/2 teaspoon baking powder**
- **1/2 teaspoon baking soda**
- **1/8 teaspoon salt**
- **2 tablespoons cold margarine, cut into small pieces**
- **1/2 cup low-fat buttermilk**

1. Preheat oven to 425°F. Spray 8 ramekins or 11×7-inch baking dish with nonstick cooking spray; place ramekins on jelly-roll pan. Set aside.

2. For filling, combine 2 tablespoons sugar and 2 tablespoons flour in large bowl. Add peaches, raspberries and lemon peel; toss to coat. Divide fruit among prepared ramekins. Bake about 15 minutes or until fruit is bubbly around edges.

3. Meanwhile, for topping, combine remaining 3/4 cup flour, 2 tablespoons sugar, baking powder, baking soda and salt in medium bowl. Cut in margarine using pastry blender or two knives until mixture resembles coarse crumbs. Stir in buttermilk just until dry ingredients are moistened.

4. Remove ramekins from oven; top fruit with equal dollops of topping. Sprinkle topping with remaining 2 teaspoons sugar. Bake 18 to 20 minutes or until topping is lightly browned. Serve warm. *Makes 8 servings*

Nutrients per Serving: 1 dessert

Calories 149	**Fiber** 3g
Fat 3g (sat 1g)	**Cholesterol** 1mg
Protein 3g	**Sodium** 195mg
Carbohydrate 28g	

Exchanges: 1 starch, 1 fruit, 1 fat

છ છ છ

Sautéed Apples Supreme

low sodium · **cooking for 1 or 2**

Quick Recipe

- **2 small apples *or* 1 large apple**
- **1 teaspoon butter**
- **1/4 cup unsweetened apple juice or cider**
- **2 teaspoons brown sugar substitute***
- **1/2 teaspoon ground cinnamon**
- **1 tablespoon chopped walnuts, toasted****

*This recipe was tested with sucralose-based sugar substitute.

**Spread nuts in shallow baking pan. Bake in preheated 350°F oven 5 to 10 minutes or until fragrant, stirring occasionally.

1. Cut apples into quarters. Core each quarter and cut into 1/2-inch-thick slices.

2. Melt butter in large nonstick skillet over medium heat. Add apples; cook 4 minutes, stirring occasionally.

3. Combine apple juice, brown sugar substitute and cinnamon; pour over apples. Simmer 5 minutes or until apples are tender and sauce thickens. Transfer to serving plates; top with walnuts. *Makes 2 servings*

Nutrients per Serving: about 3/4 cup

Calories 139	**Fiber** 4g
Fat 5g (sat 2g)	**Cholesterol** 6mg
Protein 1g	**Sodium** 22mg
Carbohydrate 26g	

Exchanges: 2 fruit, 1/2 fat

Cinnamon Tortilla with Cream Cheese & Strawberries

low fat | high fiber

Quick Recipe

1 packet sugar substitute*
1/8 teaspoon ground cinnamon
1 (6-inch) fat-free flour tortilla
  Nonstick cooking spray
1 tablespoon reduced-fat cream cheese, softened
1/3 cup fresh strawberry slices

This recipe was tested with sucralose-based sugar substitute.

1. Combine sugar substitute and cinnamon in small bowl. Lightly spray one side of tortilla with cooking spray; sprinkle with cinnamon mixture.

2. Heat large nonstick skillet over medium heat. Place tortilla, cinnamon side down, in hot skillet. Cook 2 minutes or until lightly browned. Remove from skillet.

3. Spread uncooked side of tortilla with cream cheese; arrange strawberries down center of tortilla. Roll up or fold tortilla to serve.

Makes 1 serving

Variation: Prepare recipe through step 2. Mash a few of the strawberry slices with a fork until almost smooth; stir into cream cheese. Proceed as directed in step 3.

Nutrients per Serving: 1 filled tortilla

Calories 114	**Fiber** 7g
Fat 3g (sat 2g)	**Cholesterol** 8mg
Protein 4g	**Sodium** 256mg
Carbohydrate 18g	

Exchanges: 1 starch, 1/2 fruit, 1/2 fat

Boston Babies

1 package (18-1/4 ounces) yellow cake mix
3 eggs *or* 3/4 cup cholesterol-free egg substitute
1/3 cup unsweetened applesauce
1 package (4-serving size) sugar-free vanilla pudding and pie filling mix
2 cups low-fat (1%) milk or fat-free (skim) milk
1/3 cup sugar
1/3 cup unsweetened cocoa powder
1 tablespoon cornstarch
1-1/2 cups water
1-1/2 teaspoons vanilla extract

1. Preheat oven to 350°F. Line 24 (2-1/2-inch) muffin cups with paper baking cups; set aside.

2. Prepare cake mix according to package directions using 3 eggs and applesauce. Spoon batter into prepared muffin cups. Bake according to package directions; cool completely. Freeze 12 cupcakes for another use.

3. Prepare pudding mix according to package directions using 2 cups milk; cover and refrigerate.

4. For chocolate glaze, combine sugar, cocoa, cornstarch and water in large microwavable bowl; whisk until smooth. Microwave on HIGH 4 to 6 minutes, stirring every 2 minutes, until slightly thickened. Stir in vanilla.

5. For each serving, drizzle 2 tablespoons chocolate glaze onto plate. Cut one cupcake in half; place halves on top of glaze. Top with about 2 heaping tablespoonfuls pudding. Garnish as desired. Serve immediately.

Makes 12 servings

Nutrients per Serving: 1 serving

Calories 158	**Fiber** <1g
Fat 4g (sat 1g)	**Cholesterol** 29mg
Protein 3g	**Sodium** 175mg
Carbohydrate 28g	

Exchanges: 2 starch, 1/2 fat

Chocolate Fudge Cheesecake Parfaits

(Pictured at bottom right)

- 1-1/2 cups fat-free cottage cheese
- 4 packets sugar substitute*
- 2 teaspoons packed brown sugar
- 1-1/2 teaspoons vanilla extract
- 2 tablespoons semisweet mini chocolate chips, divided
- 2 cups fat-free chocolate ice cream or fat-free frozen yogurt
- 5 tablespoons plus 1 teaspoon graham cracker crumbs
- Additional graham cracker crumbs (optional)

This recipe was tested with sucralose-based sugar substitute.

1. Combine cottage cheese, sugar substitute, brown sugar and vanilla in food processor or blender; process until smooth. Stir in 1 tablespoon mini chips.

2. Spoon about 1/4 cup ice cream into parfait glass or small bowl. Top with heaping tablespoon cheese mixture; sprinkle with 2 teaspoons graham cracker crumbs. Repeat layers. Freeze parfaits 15 to 30 minutes to firm slightly.

3. Sprinkle each parfait with remaining 1 tablespoon mini chips. Garnish with additional cracker crumbs, if desired.

Makes 4 servings

Nutrients per Serving: 1 parfait

Calories 199	**Fiber** 1g
Fat 2g (sat 1g)	**Cholesterol** 0mg
Protein 17g	**Sodium** 419mg
Carbohydrate 28g	

Exchanges: 1-1/2 starch, 1-1/2 lean meat

Pears with Sweet Strawberry Dipping Cream

Quick Recipe

- 4 ounces fresh strawberries or frozen unsweetened strawberries, thawed (about 6 strawberries)
- 1/4 cup reduced-fat spreadable cream cheese
- 1/4 cup plain fat-free yogurt
- 2 packets sugar substitute*
- 1/2 teaspoon vanilla extract
- 2 medium pears, cut in 1/2-inch slices

This recipe was tested with sucralose-based sugar substitute.

Process strawberries in food processor or blender until coarsely chopped. Add cream cheese, yogurt, sugar substitute and vanilla. Cover and process until smooth. To serve, dip pear slices in cream cheese mixture.

Makes 8 servings

Nutrients per Serving: 1 pear quarter with 1 tablespoon dipping cream

Calories 52	**Fiber** 1g
Fat 1g (sat 1g)	**Cholesterol** 4mg
Protein 2g	**Sodium** 43mg
Carbohydrate 8g	

Exchanges: 1/2 fruit, 1/2 fat

Chocolate Fudge Cheesecake Parfaits

...d figs

...ons hot water

...on granulated sugar

2/3 cup all-purpose flour

1/2 cup uncooked quick oats

3/4 teaspoon baking powder

1/4 teaspoon salt

2 tablespoons canola oil

2-1/2 to 3 tablespoons fat-free (skim) milk

1 ounce reduced-fat cream cheese, softened

1/3 cup powdered sugar

1/2 teaspoon vanilla extract

1. Preheat oven to 400°F. Lightly coat cookie sheet with nonstick cooking spray.

2. To prepare filling, combine figs, water and granulated sugar in food processor or blender; process until figs are finely chopped. Set aside.

3. To prepare dough, combine flour, oats, baking powder and salt in medium bowl. Add oil and just enough milk, 1 tablespoon at a time, until mixture forms a ball.

4. Roll dough into 12×9-inch rectangle on lightly floured surface. Place dough on prepared cookie sheet. Spread fig mixture in 2-1/2-inch-wide strip lengthwise down center of rectangle. Make cuts almost to filling at 1/2-inch intervals on both 12-inch sides. Fold strips over filling, overlapping in center to form a braid. Bake 15 to 18 minutes or until lightly browned.

5. To prepare icing, combine cream cheese, powdered sugar and vanilla in small bowl; mix well. Spread over braid. Cut into 12 pieces.

Makes 12 servings

Nutrients per Serving: 1 bar (1/12 of total recipe)

Calories 104	**Fiber** 1g
Fat 3g (sat 1g)	**Cholesterol** 1mg
Protein 2g	**Sodium** 93mg
Carbohydrate 18g	

Exchanges: 1 starch, 1/2 fat

Spiced Wafers

1/2 cup (1 stick) butter, softened

1 cup sugar

1 egg

2 tablespoons fat-free (skim) milk

1 teaspoon vanilla extract

1-3/4 cups all-purpose flour

2 teaspoons baking powder

1 teaspoon ground cinnamon

1/2 teaspoon ground nutmeg

1/4 teaspoon ground cloves

Red hot candies or red colored sugar for garnish (optional)

1. Beat butter in large bowl with electric mixer at medium speed until smooth. Add sugar; beat until well blended. Add egg, milk and vanilla; beat until well blended.

2. Combine flour, baking powder, cinnamon, nutmeg and cloves in large bowl. Gradually add flour mixture to butter mixture at low speed, blending well after each addition.

3. Shape dough into 2 logs, each about 2 inches in diameter and 6 inches long. Wrap each log in plastic wrap. Refrigerate 2 to 3 hours or overnight.

4. Preheat oven to 350°F. Spray cookie sheets with nonstick cooking spray. Cut logs into 1/4-inch slices; place 2 inches apart on cookie sheets. Decorate with candies or colored sugar, if desired.

5. Bake 11 to 13 minutes or until edges are light brown. Transfer to wire racks to cool. Store in airtight container.

Makes about 4 dozen cookies

Nutrients per Serving: 1 cookie

Calories 52	**Fiber** <1g
Fat 2g (sat 1g)	**Cholesterol** 10mg
Protein 1g	**Sodium** 37mg
Carbohydrate 8g	

Exchanges: 1/2 starch, 1/2 fat

Sweet Potato Phyllo Wraps

(Pictured below)

3/4 cup mashed sweet potato

3/4 teaspoon vanilla extract

1/2 teaspoon ground cinnamon

4 (14×9-inch) sheets frozen phyllo dough, thawed

Butter-flavored cooking spray

4 tablespoons finely chopped pecans

1 tablespoon light maple syrup

Fresh strawberries (optional)

1. Preheat oven to 375°F. Line baking sheet with parchment paper. Combine sweet potato, vanilla and cinnamon in small bowl; mix well.

2. Unroll phyllo dough, keeping sheets in a stack. Cover with large sheet of waxed paper and damp kitchen towel. Remove one sheet at a time; place on work surface. Spray edges lightly with cooking spray.

3. Spread 3 tablespoons sweet potato mixture across short edge of phyllo dough. Sprinkle with 1 tablespoon chopped pecans. Roll up. Cut into thirds; place on prepared baking sheet. Repeat with remaining phyllo sheets, sweet potato mixture and pecans.

4. Spray tops of wraps with cooking spray. Bake 15 to 20 minutes or until golden brown. Remove from oven; drizzle with maple syrup. Garnish with strawberries, if desired.

Makes 4 servings

Nutrients per Serving: 3 wraps with 3/4 teaspoon maple syrup

Calories 165	**Fiber** 3g
Fat 7g (sat 1g)	**Cholesterol** 0mg
Protein 3g	**Sodium** 120mg
Carbohydrate 24g	

Exchanges: 1-1/2 starch, 1 fat

Sweet Potato Phyllo Wraps

Chocolate Swirl Cheesecake

Chocolate Swirl Cheesecake

low carb

(Pictured above)

1-1/4 cups vanilla wafer crumbs

4 tablespoons stick butter or margarine, melted

2 tablespoons EQUAL® SPOONFUL*

3 packages (8 ounces each) reduced-fat cream cheese, softened

3/4 cup EQUAL® SPOONFUL**

2 eggs

2 egg whites

2 tablespoons cornstarch

1 cup reduced-fat sour cream

1 teaspoon vanilla

1 ounce unsweetened chocolate, melted, slightly cooled

1 tablespoon skim milk

Chocolate curls (optional)

May substitute 3 packets EQUAL® sweetener.

**May substitute 18 packets EQUAL® sweetener.*

• Mix vanilla wafer crumbs, butter and 2 tablespoons Equal® Spoonful in bottom of 9-inch springform pan. Pat mixture evenly on bottom and 1/2 inch up side of pan. Bake in preheated 325°F oven 10 minutes. Cool on wire rack while preparing filling.

• Beat cream cheese and 3/4 cup Equal® Spoonful in large bowl until fluffy; beat in eggs, egg whites and cornstarch. Stir in sour cream and vanilla until well blended. Remove 1/2 cup cheesecake batter. Pour remaining batter into crust in pan.

• Add melted chocolate and skim milk to 1/2 cup reserved cheesecake batter; mix well. Place spoonfuls of chocolate mixture on top of cheesecake. Using tip of knife or spatula, gently swirl chocolate batter into cheesecake.

• Bake in 325°F oven 45 to 50 minutes or until center is almost set. Remove cheesecake to wire rack. Gently run metal spatula around rim of pan to loosen cheesecake. Let cheesecake cool completely; cover and refrigerate several hours or overnight before serving. To serve, remove sides of springform pan. Garnish top of cheesecake with chocolate curls, if desired.

Makes 16 servings

Nutrients per Serving: 1 slice cheesecake (1/16 of total recipe)

Calories 164	**Fiber** <1g
Fat 11g (sat 8g)	**Cholesterol** 57mg
Protein 7g	**Sodium** 235mg
Carbohydrate 8g	

Exchanges: 1/2 starch, 2 fat

Tip

Soften the cream cheese before beginning this recipe to prevent lumps from forming in the batter. Also, softened cream cheese will easily combine with the other ingredients without overbeating. Be sure to avoid overbeating because it can cause the cheesecake to crack.

Acknowledgments

**The publisher would like to thank the companies and organizations
listed below for the use of their recipes and photographs
in this publication.**

Birds Eye Foods

Cabot® Creamery Cooperative

California Dried Plum Board

California Olive Industry

California Tree Fruit Agreement

Del Monte Corporation

Equal® sweetener

Minnesota Cultivated Wild Rice Council

National Cattlemen's Beef Association on behalf of The Beef Checkoff

National Honey Board

National Turkey Federation

Peanut Advisory Board

Reckitt Benckiser Inc.

The Sugar Association, Inc.

Reprinted with permission of Sunkist Growers, Inc. All Rights Reserved.

General Index

Icon Index

LOW-FAT

LOW-SODIUM

meatless
MEATLESS

COOKING FOR
1 OR 2

METRIC CONVERSION CHART

VOLUME MEASUREMENTS (dry)

⅛ teaspoon = 0.5 mL
¼ teaspoon = 1 mL
½ teaspoon = 2 mL
¾ teaspoon = 4 mL
1 teaspoon = 5 mL
1 tablespoon = 15 mL
2 tablespoons = 30 mL
¼ cup = 60 mL
⅓ cup = 75 mL
½ cup = 125 mL
⅔ cup = 150 mL
¾ cup = 175 mL
1 cup = 250 mL
2 cups = 1 pint = 500 mL
3 cups = 750 mL
4 cups = 1 quart = 1 L

VOLUME MEASUREMENTS (fluid)

1 fluid ounce (2 tablespoons) = 30 mL
4 fluid ounces (½ cup) = 125 mL
8 fluid ounces (1 cup) = 250 mL
12 fluid ounces (1½ cups) = 375 mL
16 fluid ounces (2 cups) = 500 mL

WEIGHTS (mass)

½ ounce = 15 g
1 ounce = 30 g
3 ounces = 90 g
4 ounces = 120 g
8 ounces = 225 g
10 ounces = 285 g
12 ounces = 360 g
16 ounces = 1 pound = 450 g

DIMENSIONS

1/16 inch = 2 mm
⅛ inch = 3 mm
¼ inch = 6 mm
½ inch = 1.5 cm
¾ inch = 2 cm
1 inch = 2.5 cm

OVEN TEMPERATURES

250°F = 120°C
275°F = 140°C
300°F = 150°C
325°F = 160°C
350°F = 180°C
375°F = 190°C
400°F = 200°C
425°F = 220°C
450°F = 230°C

BAKING PAN SIZES

Utensil	Size in Inches/Quarts	Metric Volume	Size in Centimeters
Baking or Cake Pan (square or rectangular)	8×8×2	2 L	20×20×5
	9×9×2	2.5 L	23×23×5
	12×8×2	3 L	30×20×5
	13×9×2	3.5 L	33×23×5
Loaf Pan	8×4×3	1.5 L	20×10×7
	9×5×3	2 L	23×13×7
Round Layer Cake Pan	8×1½	1.2 L	20×4
	9×1½	1.5 L	23×4
Pie Plate	8×1¼	750 mL	20×3
	9×1¼	1 L	23×3
Baking Dish or Casserole	1 quart	1 L	—
	1½ quart	1.5 L	—
	2 quart	2 L	—